Bookkeeping Controls

Workbook

David Cox
Michael Fardon

Published by Osborne Books Limited
Tel 01905 748071
Email books@osbornebooks.co.uk
Website www.osbornebooks.co.uk

Design by Laura Ingham

Printed by CPI Group (UK) Limited, Croydon, CR0 4YY, on environmentally friendly, acid-free paper from managed forests.

British Library Cataloguing in Publication Data
A catalogue record for this book is available from the British Library

ISBN 978 1909173 682

Contents

Introduction

Chapter activities

Answers to chapter activities

Practice assessments – tasks

Answers to practice assessments

Also available from Osborne Books...

Tutorials

Clear, explanatory books written
precisely to the specifications

Wise Guides

Handy pocket-sized study and revision guides

Student Zone

Login to access your free ebooks and
interactive revision crosswords

Download **Osborne Books App** free from the App Store or Google Play Store
to view your ebooks online or offline on your mobile or tablet.

www.osbornebooks.co.uk

Introduction

Qualifications covered

This book has been written specifically to cover the Unit 'Bookkeeping Controls' which is mandatory for the following qualifications:

AAT Foundation Certificate in Accounting – Level 2

AAT Foundation Diploma in Accounting and Business – Level 2

AAT Foundation Certificate in Bookkeeping – Level 2

AAT Foundation Certificate in Accounting at SCQF Level 5

This book contains Chapter Activities which provide extra practice material in addition to the activities included in the Osborne Books Tutorial text, and Practice Assessments to prepare the student for the computer based assessments. The latter are based directly on the structure, style and content of the sample assessment material provided by the AAT at www.aat.org.uk.

Suggested answers to the Chapter Activities and Practice Assessments are set out in this book.

Osborne Study and Revision Materials

The materials featured on the previous page are tailored to the needs of students studying this Unit and revising for the assessment. They include:

- **Tutorials:** paperback books with practice activities
- **Wise Guides:** pocket-sized spiral bound revision cards
- **Student Zone:** access to Osborne Books online resources
- **Osborne Books App:** Osborne Books ebooks for mobiles and tablets

Visit www.osbornebooks.co.uk for details of study and revision resources and access to online material.

Chapter
activities

1 Payment methods

1.1 Cash can be used as a form of payment in which **two** of the following situations?

(a) Employee wages	
(b) BACS transfers	
(c) A petty cash system	
(d) Payment using chip and PIN	

1.2 If you are asked to make a payment by post you are most likely to use which **one** of the following methods?

(a) CHAPS	
(b) Cheque	
(c) Direct debit	
(d) Contactless card	

1.3 Draw lines connecting the four methods of card payment listed on the left with the correct descriptions in the boxes on the right.

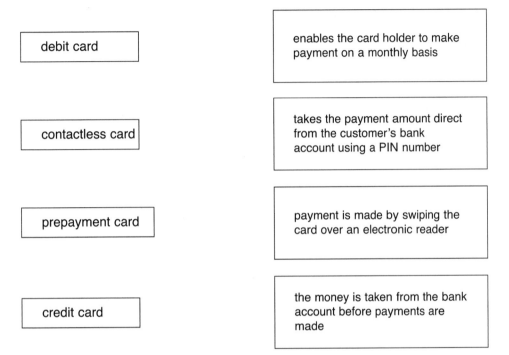

debit card		enables the card holder to make payment on a monthly basis
contactless card		takes the payment amount direct from the customer's bank account using a PIN number
prepayment card		payment is made by swiping the card over an electronic reader
credit card		the money is taken from the bank account before payments are made

1.4 For a cheque to be a valid method of payment it has to comply with certain conditions. Indicate in the table below whether the following statements are true or false.

Statement	True	False
(a) A cheque has to be dated within seven days of making the payment		
(b) A cheque has to be signed by the person making payment		
(c) A cheque has to be signed by the person paying it into the bank		
(d) A cheque has to be paid in within a month of the date written on the top of the cheque		

1.5   Complete the text below by using the appropriate words from the following list:

standing order   **direct debit**

receiver's bank   **variable amounts**

payer's bank

A [   ] is set up by the [   ] and used to make regular electronic payments for the same amount through the banking system.

A [   ] on the other hand enables [   ] to be taken from the payer's account and the payments are deducted by the

[   ] .

1.6   You are running a business and have just signed a lease on a rented office. You are incurring various expenses in connection with the office. Which method of payment from the list provided at the end of the question would you choose as the best to use in the situations listed below? Enter the number of the most appropriate payment option in the table below.

	Option number
(a) Paying rent for the office at a fixed amount of £750 a month	
(b) Paying insurance premium of £2,000 which increases every year	
(c) Buying office furniture for £1,200 from a local superstore	
(d) Paying solicitors fees of £500 plus VAT in connection with lease	
(e) Buying a travel card for £30 at the local railway station	

List of payment options – enter the option number in the appropriate box in the table above.

1   contactless payment card

3   business credit card

4   direct debit

5   Faster Payment

6   standing order

1.7   You work in a finance office and are checking the payments received from customers. The payments include cheques.

(a)   You are to identify three errors on the cheque shown below. Write down the errors in the table below.

Southern Bank PLC Mereford Branch 16 Broad Street, Mereford MR1 7TR	date **2 June**	97-76-54
Pay **J M Supplies Ltd**		only
Four hundred pounds only	Account payee only	**£ 420.00**
		T WITT TRADING LTD
123456 977654 12963455		Director

Error 1	
Error 2	
Error 3	

(b)   What action would you take when you had discovered the errors? Choose the correct option.

(a) Correct the errors and pay the cheque into the bank	
(b) Contact T Witt Trading Ltd and ask for a new cheque to be issued	
(c) Pay the cheque into the bank and hope that the errors will not be noticed	

2 Payment methods and the bank account balance

2.1 Money paid into the bank account of a business earlier rather than later improves which **three** of the following listed below?

(a) The solvency of the business	
(b) The amount of VAT payable to HMRC	
(c) The contribution of the business to the principle of sustainability	
(d) Keeping bank charges to a minimum	
(e) Keeping interest payable on overdrafts to a minimum	

2.2 Good practice in the management of the bank account of a business should involve which **three** of the following options?

(a) Keeping the bank account in credit whenever possible	
(b) Paying in cheques as late as possible	
(c) Encouraging customers to pay accounts due by Faster Payment	
(d) Paying wages in cash rather than by BACS credit	
(e) Paying the business insurance costs by direct debit rather than in a lump sum at the beginning of the period of insurance	

2.3 It is important to appreciate that a 'credit balance' and a 'debit balance' mean opposite things when used by:

(a)   a business describing the bank account in its cash book

(b)   its bank describing the account held by the business and as shown on the bank statement received from the bank

Complete the table below indicating in the column on the right whether the statement on the left will result in a debit or credit entry.

Situation	Debit or credit?
(a) Money paid **into** the bank account as shown in the cash book of the business	
(b) Money paid **into** the bank account as shown on the bank statement	
(c) A payment **out of** the bank account as shown in the cash book of the business	
(d) A payment **out of** the bank account as shown on the bank statement	

2.4 Which **three** of the payment methods listed below will **reduce** the balance of the payer's account held at the bank on the day that the payment is made?

Tick the appropriate options.

(a) Faster payment	
(b) Cheque payment	
(c) CHAPS	
(d) Direct debit	
(e) Prepayment card	

2.5 Which **two** of the payment methods listed below will **not reduce** the balance of the payer's account held at the bank on the day that the payment is made?

Tick the appropriate options.

(a)	Debit card	
(b)	Bank draft	
(c)	Cash wages	
(d)	Credit card	
(e)	Standing order	

2.6 Draw lines connecting the four methods of payment listed on the left with the appropriate period of time it will normally take for the amount to be deducted from the bank account of the payer.

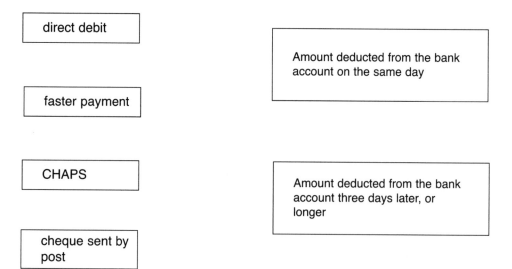

direct debit

faster payment

CHAPS

cheque sent by post

Amount deducted from the bank account on the same day

Amount deducted from the bank account three days later, or longer

2.7   A business receives an invoice from a supplier. The invoice terms are payment within 30 days of the invoice date. There is no early settlement discount offered. The invoice includes the bank account details of the supplier and payment by electronic transfer is requested.

In order to keep the bank account balance as high as it can for as long as it can the business will adopt its normal practice and pay the invoice by Faster Payment.

Which **one** of the three options shown below should the business choose to pay the invoice?

(a)	Pay the invoice in the week after it has been received	
(b)	Pay the invoice so that it reaches the supplier's bank as late as possible within the 30 days limit	
(c)	Pay the invoice as soon as a chaser for non-payment is received from the supplier after the 30 day period has elapsed	

3 Bank reconciliation statements

3.1 Upon receipt of a bank statement, which **one** of the following must be written into the firm's cash book?

(a) Payment debited in error by the bank	
(b) Unpresented cheques	
(c) Automated transfers from customers	
(d) Outstanding lodgements	

3.2 A firm's bank statement shows an overdraft of £600. Unpresented cheques total £250; outstanding lodgements total £1,000. What is the balance at bank shown by the cash book?

(a) £150 debit	
(b) £650 debit	
(c) £250 credit	
(d) £150 credit	

3.3   Show whether the following statements are true or false.

Statement		True	False
(a)	Some differences between the bank statement and the cash book are described as timing differences – these are not corrected in the cash book		
(b)	A trade receivable's cheque has been dishonoured and returned by the bank – the amount of the returned cheque must be recorded in cash book on the debit side		
(c)	In a bank reconciliation statement which starts with the balance as per bank statement, unpresented cheques are deducted		
(d)	The opening cash book balance at bank will always be the same as the opening bank statement balance		

3.4   Complete the following text by choosing the correct words from the boxes below and entering them in the boxes in the text.

cash book	bank statement	ledger	error
discrepancy	fraud	regular	daily
timing	date	independent	similarity

It is important to reconcile the cash book to the [　　　　　　　　　　　　　　　]

on a [　　　　　　　　　　　　] basis.

The bank statement provides an [　　　　　　　　　　　　　] accounting

record and helps to prevent [　　　　　　　　　　] .

It also highlights any [　　　　　　　　　　　] differences and explains

why there is a [　　　　　　　　　] between the bank statement

balance and the [　　　　　　　　] balance.

3.5   The bank statement and cash book for June are shown below and on the next page.

    (a)   Check the bank statement against the cash book and enter:

        •   any transactions into the cash book as needed

        •   the cash book balance carried down at 30 June and brought down at 1 July.

BANK STATEMENT				
Date 20-4	Details	Paid out £	Paid in £	Balance £
01 Jun	Balance b/f			2,685 C
02 Jun	Cheque 784342	855		1,830 C
07 Jun	BACS credit: P Parker		1,525	3,355 C
08 Jun	Cheque 784344	697		2,658 C
10 Jun	Cheque 784345	1,922		736 C
14 Jun	Counter credit		2,607	3,343 C
15 Jun	Cheque 784343	412		2,931 C
18 Jun	BACS credit: Watson Ltd		2,109	5,040 C
24 Jun	Direct debit: First Electric	112		4,928 C
24 Jun	Cheque 784347	1,181		3,747 C
25 Jun	Bank charges	45		3,702 C
28 Jun	Cheque 784348	594		3,108 C
D = Debit C = Credit				

CASH BOOK

Date 20-4	Details	Bank £	Date 20-4	Cheque number	Details	Bank £
1 Jun	Balance b/f	1,830	3 Jun	784343	Gladysz & Co	412
5 Jun	P Parker	1,525	3 Jun	784344	Daley Ltd	697
10 Jun	Dunlevy Ltd	2,607	3 Jun	784345	Ward & Lamb	1,922
25 Jun	Corline Traders	1,433	12 Jun	784346	Hendrie Stores	692
28 Jun	Moss & Co	786	12 Jun	784347	McCabes	1,181
			12 Jun	784348	Rehman Ltd	594
			24 Jun		First Electric	112
			29 Jun	784349	Hannaford & Co	764

Tutorial note: there is an opening balance difference.

Select your entries for the details column from the following list: Balance b/d, Balance c/d, Bank charges, Closing balance, Corline Traders, Daley Ltd, Dunlevy Ltd, First Electric, Gladysz & Co, Hannaford & Co, Hendrie Stores, McCabes, Moss & Co, Opening balance, P Parker, Rehman Ltd, Ward & Lamb, Watson Ltd.

continued

(b)   Complete the bank reconciliation statement as at 30 June.

Select your entries from the following list: Bank charges, Corline Traders, Daley Ltd, Dunlevy Ltd, First Electric, Gladysz & Co, Hannaford & Co, Hendrie Stores, McCabes, Moss & Co, P Parker, Rehman Ltd, Ward & Lamb, Watson Ltd.

Bank reconciliation statement	£
Balance as per bank statement	
Add	
Total to add	
Less	
Total to subtract	
Balance as per cash book	

3.6   Complete the following text by choosing the correct words from the boxes below and entering them in the boxes in the text.

cash book	timing differences	bank	errors

security	reconciliation	authorised

The bank [   ] explains any difference between the

balance in the [   ] and the balance at the

[   ] .

It highlights any [   ] and [   ] .

Access to bank records should be restricted to [   ]

employees to safeguard the [   ] of payments and receipts.

4 Using control accounts

4.1 You have the following information for the month:

• customer balances at start of month	£25,685
• credit sales	£18,732
• sales returns	£876
• money received from customers	£17,455
• discounts allowed	£227
• irrecoverable debt written off	£175

What is the figure for customer balances at the end of the month?

(a) £23,130	
(b) £25,684	
(c) £25,686	
(d) £26,034	

4.2 You have the following information for the month:

• supplier balances at start of month	£13,278
• credit purchases	£9,584
• purchases returns	£821
• money paid to suppliers	£10,058
• discounts received	£247

What is the figure for supplier balances at the end of the month?

(a) £12,230	
(b) £13,378	
(c) £11,736	
(d) £14,820	

4.3   You have the following information for the month:

- balance of VAT account at start of month   £2,380   credit
- VAT from sales day book   £1,420
- VAT from purchases day book   £1,030
- VAT from discounts allowed day book   £35
- VAT from sales returns day book   £223
- VAT from purchases returns day book   £185
- VAT from discounts received day book   £22
- VAT from cash sales   £570

What is the balance of VAT account at the end of the month?

(a) £1,471 debit	
(b) £1,471 credit	
(c) £3,289 debit	
(d) £3,289 credit	

4.4   **(a)**   The following is a summary of transactions with credit customers during the month of July.

Show by ticking the appropriate column whether each entry will be a debit or credit in the sales ledger control account in the general ledger.

Sales ledger control account

Details	Amount £	Debit	Credit
Balance owing from credit customers at 1 July	7,298		
Money received from credit customers	6,450		
Discounts allowed	75		
Goods sold to credit customers	14,774		
Goods returned by credit customers	501		
Journal credit to correct an error	89		

(b)   The following is a summary of transactions with credit suppliers during the month of July.

Show by ticking the appropriate column whether each entry will be a debit or credit in the purchases ledger control account in the general ledger.

Purchases ledger control account

Details	Amount £	Debit	Credit
Balance owing to credit suppliers at 1 July	2,299		
Money paid to credit suppliers	2,276		
Discounts received	23		
Goods purchased from credit suppliers	5,113		
Goods returned to credit suppliers	108		

At the beginning of September the following balances were in the sales ledger:

Credit customers	Balances	
	Amount £	Debit/credit
J Stone	1,992	Debit
Murray Ltd	2,464	Debit
Parton & Co	320	Credit
Davies Ltd	411	Debit
Carpenter Ltd	2,569	Debit
King & Co	1,945	Debit

(c)   What should the balance of the sales ledger control account be on 1 September in order for it to reconcile with the total of the balances in the sales ledger?

Balance	
(a) Debit balance of £9,701	
(b) Credit balance of £9,701	
(c) Debit balance of £9,061	
(d) Credit balance of £9,061	

(d) Show whether the following statements are true or false.

	True	False
(a) If an irrecoverable debt is not written off in the sales ledger control account, the balance on the account will be lower than it should be		
(b) The balance of the purchases ledger control account should agree to the total of the aged trade payables analysis		
(c) Reconciliation of the sales ledger control account highlights any differences between the subsidiary ledger total and the control account balance		

4.5   You work as an accounts assistant for Tilsley Trading. Today you are working on the purchases ledger control account and purchases ledger.

A summary of transactions with credit suppliers during the month of June is shown below.

(a)   Show whether each entry will be a debit or a credit in the purchases ledger control account in the general ledger.

Details	Amount £	Debit	Credit
Balance of credit suppliers at 1 June	35,106		
Purchases from credit suppliers	20,354		
Payments made to credit suppliers	19,062		
Discounts received	289		
Goods returned to credit suppliers	1,374		

(b)   What will be the balance brought down on 1 July on the above account?

(a) Dr £34,735	
(b) Cr £34,735	
(c) Dr £35,477	
(d) Cr £35,477	
(e) Dr £35,313	
(f) Cr £35,313	

The following credit balances were in the purchases ledger on 1 July.

	£
Cockerill Ltd	9,262
Darnbrook & Co	3,495
M Warren	5,724
De Graaf Ltd	6,098
Hannaford Trading	4,477
Quesne plc	5,386

(c)   Reconcile the balances shown above with the purchases ledger control account balance calculated in part (b).

	£
Balance on purchases ledger control account at 1 July	
Total of the purchases ledger balances at 1 July	
Difference	

(d)   What may have caused the difference you calculated in part (c)?

(a) An amount for discounts received was entered twice in the purchases ledger control account	
(b) A credit note was not entered in the purchases ledger control account	
(c) A credit note was not entered in the purchases ledger	
(d) An amount for discounts received was not entered in the purchases ledger	

4.6   You work as an Accounts Assistant for Wyvern Windows. Today you are working on the sales ledger control account and sales ledger. A summary of transactions with credit customers during the month of April is shown below.

(a)   Show whether each entry will be a debit or a credit in the sales ledger control account in the general ledger.

Details	Amount	Debit	Credit
	£		
Balance of credit customers at 1 April	18,392		
Goods sold to credit customers	6,874		
Money received from credit customers	8,937		
Discounts allowed	154		
Goods returned by credit customers	529		

(b)   What will be the balance brought down on 1 May on the above account?

(a) Dr £17,012	
(b) Cr £17,012	
(c) Dr £15,646	
(d) Cr £15,646	
(e) Dr £21,138	
(f) Cr £21,138	

The following debit balances were in the sales ledger on 1 May.

	£
Hamilton Ltd	3,486
Gusson & Co	1,089
Palgrave Supplies	2,627
Ikpusu & Co	4,321
Lorenz Ltd	747
McDiarmid plc	3,961

(c)   Reconcile the balances shown above with the sales ledger control account balance calculated in part (b).

	£
Balance on sales ledger control account at 1 May	
Total of the sales ledger balances at 1 May	
Difference	

(d)   What may have caused the difference you calculated in part (c)?

(a) An invoice was entered twice in the sales ledger	
(b) A credit note was entered twice in the sales ledger	
(c) A credit note was not entered in the sales ledger control account	
(d) An amount of discounts allowed was not entered in the sales ledger control account	

(e)   Tick **two** of the following statements that are true.

(a) Reconciliation of the purchases ledger control account assures managers that the amount showing as outstanding to suppliers is correct	
(b) The balance of the purchases ledger control account should agree to the total of the balances in the sales ledger	
(c) The balance of the sales ledger control account should agree to the total of the aged trade payables analysis	
(d) Reconciliation of the sales ledger control account highlights any differences between the subsidiary ledger total and the control account balance	

4.7 You work as an Accounts Assistant for Craven Cottages Ltd. Today you are working on the VAT control account.

The following figures have been taken from Craven Cottages' books of prime entry:

Totals for quarter

Sales day book	
Net	£68,800
VAT	£13,760
Total	£82,560

Purchases day book	
Net	£35,000
VAT	£7,000
Total	£42,000

Sales returns day book	
Net	£2,240
VAT	£448
Total	£2,688

Purchases returns day book	
Net	£1,640
VAT	£328
Total	£1,968

Cash book: cash-sales	
Net	£2,840
VAT	£568
Total	£3,408

Discounts allowed day book	
Net	£600
VAT	£120
Total	£720

(a) What will be the entries in the VAT control account to record the VAT transactions in the quarter?

Select your entries for the details columns from the following list: Cash sales, Discounts allowed, Discounts allowed day book, Purchases, Purchases day book, Purchases returns, Purchases returns day book, Sales, Sales day book, Sales returns, Sales returns day book, Value Added Tax.

VAT control account

Details	Amount £	Details	Amount £

(b) The VAT Return has been completed and shows an amount owing to HM Revenue & Customs of £6,432.

Is the VAT Return correct?

Yes	
No	

4.8 The following is a list of the VAT totals from the books of prime entry of a business:

Books of prime entry	**VAT totals for quarter**
	£
Sales day book	14,800
Purchases day book	9,080
Sales returns day book	368
Purchases returns day book	248
Cash book: cash sales	376

Other VAT items for the quarter are as follows:

VAT on petty cash payments	17
VAT on irrecoverable debts written off	108
VAT on purchase of computer equipment	575
VAT paid to HMRC	9,804

(a) What will be the entries in the VAT control account to record the VAT transactions in the quarter?

Select your entries for the details column from the following list: Bank, Cash sales, Computer equipment, Irrecoverable debts, Petty cash, Purchases, Purchases day book, Purchases returns, Purchases returns day book, Sales, Sales day book, Sales returns, Sales returns day book, VAT.

VAT control account

Details	Amount £	Details	Amount £
		Balance b/f	9,804

(b) The VAT Return has been completed and shows an amount owing to HM Revenue & Customs of £5,276.

Is the VAT Return correct?

Yes	
No	

(c) Show whether the following statements are true or false.

	True	False
(a) The VAT control account is used to calculate how much VAT is due to, or sometimes from, HM Revenue & Customs		
(b) A debit balance on the VAT control account indicates that the business is due a refund from HM Revenue & Customs		
(c) A bank payment of VAT due to HM Revenue & Customs will be entered as a debit in the VAT control account		

4.9 The following is a record of the VAT values in the books of prime entry of a business:

	£
VAT from Sales day book	17,080
VAT from Sales returns day book	280
VAT from Purchases day book	9,800
VAT from Purchases returns day book	760
VAT from Discounts received day book	120
VAT from Cash book (VAT on cash sales)	192
VAT on petty cash payments	9
VAT on irrecoverable debt written off	82
VAT on purchase of studio equipment	400
VAT paid to HMRC	6,536

(a) What will be the entries in the VAT control account to record the VAT transactions in the quarter?

Select your entries for the details columns from the following list: Bank, Cash book, Discounts received, Discounts received day book, Irrecoverable debts, Petty cash, Purchases, Purchases returns, Sales, Sales returns, Studio equipment, VAT.

VAT control account

Details	Amount £	Details	Amount £
		Balance b/f	6,536

The VAT Return has been completed and shows an amount owing to HM Revenue & Customs of £7,581.

(b) Is the VAT Return correct?

Yes	
No	

(c) Show whether the following statements are true or false.

	True	False
(a) VAT on purchases and expenses can only be entered in the VAT account if the purchase document bears the VAT registration number of the supplier		
(b) A bank receipt of a refund of VAT from HM Revenue & Customs would be shown as a credit in the VAT control account		
(c) A bank payment of VAT due to HM Revenue & Customs will be entered as a credit in the VAT control account		

5 The journal

5.1 Which **one** of the following transactions will be recorded in the journal?

(a) Purchase of goods on credit	
(b) Payroll transactions	
(c) Goods returned by a credit customer	
(d) Sale of goods for cash	

5.2 Mohammed Pazir started in business on 1 February 20-4 with the following assets and liabilities:

	£
Vehicle	6,500
Fixtures and fittings	2,800
Inventory	4,100
Cash	150
Bank	1,250
Loan from uncle	5,000

Use the form below to prepare Mohammed's opening journal entry, showing clearly his capital at 1 February 20-4.

Date 20-4	Details	Reference	Dr £	Cr £
	Journal entries to record the opening entries of the new business.			

5.3   You are employed by Sachdev Supplies as an Accounts Assistant. Today the Accounts Supervisor tells you that a credit customer, Lefroy Limited, has ceased trading, owing Sachdev Supplies £560 plus VAT at 20%.

(a)   Record the journal entries needed in the general ledger to write off the net amount and the VAT.

Select your account names from the following list: Irrecoverable debts, Lefroy Limited, Purchases, Purchases ledger control, Sachdev Supplies, Sales, Sales ledger control, Value Added Tax.

Account name	Debit £	Credit £

(b)   Sachdev Supplies has started a new business, Sachdev Developments, and a new set of accounts is to be opened. A partially completed journal to record the opening entries is shown below.

Record the journal entries needed in the accounts in the general ledger of Sachdev Developments to deal with the opening entries.

Account name	Amount £	Debit	Credit
Sales ledger control	14,275		
Purchases ledger control	7,392		
Inventory	4,107		
Office equipment	10,400		
Cash at bank	2,822		
Rent and rates	4,086		
Miscellaneous expenses	794		
Wages	2,397		
Loan from bank	6,250		
Capital	25,239		
Journal entries to record the opening entries of the new business			

5.4   You are employed by Mullen Limited as an Accounts Assistant.

Mullen Limited pays its employees through the bank every month and maintains a wages control account. A summary of last month's payroll transactions is shown below.

Item	£
Wages expense*	24,489
Income tax	2,510
Employer's National Insurance contributions	1,105
Employees' National Insurance contributions	965
Employer's pension contributions	1,032
Employees' pension contributions	1,032

*__Tutorial note__: Wages expense is the total cost of the payroll to the employer, that is gross wages of employees (before deductions) + employer's NIC + employer's pension contributions.

Show the journal entries needed to record:

•   the wages expense

•   the HM Revenue & Customs liability

•   the net wages paid to employees

•   the pension fund liability

Select your account names from the following list: Bank, Employees' National Insurance, Employer's National Insurance, HM Revenue & Customs, Income tax, Net wages, Pension fund, Wages control, Wages expense.

Journal to record the wages expense

Account name	Debit £	Credit £

Journal to record the HM Revenue & Customs liability

Account name	Debit £	Credit £

Journal to record the net wages paid to employees

Account name	Debit £	Credit £

Journal to record the pension fund liability

Account name	Debit £	Credit £

5.5 Show which **four** of the following transactions would be entered in the journal.

(a)	Bank loan repayment	
(b)	Irrecoverable debt written off	
(c)	Opening entries at start of business	
(d)	Payment of VAT owing to HMRC	
(e)	Payroll transactions	
(f)	Purchase of non-current assets	
(g)	Transfer of cash from cash sales to bank	

6 The trial balance and correction of errors

6.1 Fill in the missing words from the following sentences, choosing from:

omission   commission   principle   original entry   reversal of entries   compensating

(a) "You made an error of [   ] when you debited the cost of diesel fuel for the van to Vans Account."

(b) "I've had an email from the accounts supervisor at Jones Limited concerning the statements of account that we sent out the other day. She says that there is a sales invoice charged that she knows nothing about. I wonder if it should be for T Jones' account and we have made an error of [   ]?"

(c) "There is a 'bad figure' on a purchases invoice – we have read it as £35 when it should be £55. It has gone through our accounts wrongly so we have an error of [   ] [   ] to put right."

(d) "Although the trial balance balanced last week, I've since found an error of £100 in the calculation of the balance of sales account. We will need to check the other balances as I think we may have a [   ] error."

(e) "Who was in charge of that trainee last week? He has entered the payment for the electricity bill on the debit side of the bank and on the credit side of electricity – a [   ]."

(f) "I found this purchase invoice from last week in amongst the copy statements. As we haven't put it through the accounts we have an error of [   ]."

6.2 Telephone expenses of £250 paid from the bank have been debited to the bank columns of the cash book and credited to the telephone expenses account. Which **one** of the following entries will correct the error?

Debit			Credit		
(a) Bank	£250		Telephone expenses	£250	
(b) Telephone expenses	£250		Bank	£250	
(c) Bank	£250		Telephone expenses	£250	
Bank	£250		Telephone expenses	£250	
(d) Telephone expenses	£250		Bank	£250	
Telephone expenses	£250		Bank	£250	

6.3 The trial balance of Tairo Traders does not balance. The debit column totals £220,472 and the credit column totals £217,647.

(a)   What entry will be made in the suspense account to balance the trial balance?

Account name	Debit £	Credit £
Suspense		

continued

(b)   It is important to understand the effects of errors in a bookkeeping system.

Show which of the errors below will cause an imbalance in the trial balance by placing a tick in the appropriate column for each error.

Error	Will cause an imbalance in the trial balance	Will not cause an imbalance in the trial balance
(a) The cost of diesel fuel, £50, has been debited in the cash book and credited to vehicles account		
(b) A credit sale of £225 has not been entered in the accounts		
(c) The balance of wages account has been calculated incorrectly		
(d) A cash purchase of £85 has been recorded in the cash book only		
(e) The cost of stationery, £54, has been recorded as £45 in the cash book and stationery account		
(f) Rent paid of £450 has been debited to rent paid account and debited in the cash book		

6.4   The initial trial balance of Merrett Marketing at 30 June 20-3 did not balance. The difference of £424 was placed into a suspense account.

The error has been traced to the purchases day book as shown below.

Purchases day book

Date 20-3	Details	Invoice number	Total £	VAT £	Net £
30 Jun	Downing Traders	2798	720	120	600
30 Jun	Morwenna and Co	M/2348	576	96	480
30 Jun	Oades plc	4592	1,248	208	1,040
	Totals		2,120	424	2,120

(a)   Identify the error and record the journal entries needed in the general ledger to:
  - remove the incorrect entry
  - record the correct entry
  - remove the suspense account balance

Select your account name from the following list: Downing Traders, Morwenna and Co, Oades plc, Purchases, Purchases day book, Purchases ledger control, Purchases returns, Purchases returns day book, Sales, Sales day book, Sales ledger control, Sales returns, Sales returns day book, Suspense, Value Added Tax.

Journal to remove the incorrect entry

Account name	Debit £	Credit £

Journal to record the correct entry

Account name	Debit £	Credit £

Journal to remove the suspense account balance

Account name	Debit £	Credit £

An entry to record a bank payment of £525 for rent paid has been reversed.

(b)   Record the journal entries needed in the general ledger to:

•   remove the incorrect entry

•   record the correct entry

Select your account names from the following list: Bank, Cash, Purchases, Purchases ledger control, Rent, Sales, Sales ledger control, Suspense, Value Added Tax.

Journal to remove the incorrect entry

Account name	Debit £	Credit £

Journal to record the correct entry

Account name	Debit £	Credit £

6.5   A direct debit for business rates of £609 has been entered in the accounts as £690.

    (a)   Record the journal entries needed in the general ledger to remove the incorrect entry.

        Select your account names from the following list: Bank, Cash, Direct debit, Purchases, Rates, Suspense.

Account name	Debit £	Credit £

    (b)   Record the journal entries needed in the general ledger to record the correct entry.

        Select your account names from the following list: Bank, Cash, Direct debit, Purchases, Rates, Suspense.

Account name	Debit £	Credit £

6.6 The trial balance of Fayer and Co included a suspense account. All the bookkeeping errors have now been traced and the journal entries shown below have been recorded.

Journal entries

Account name	Debit £	Credit £
Office expenses	180	
Office equipment		180
Sales returns	295	
Suspense		295
Vehicle expenses	350	
Suspense		350

As the accounts assistant at Fayer and Co, you are to post the journal entries to the general ledger accounts. Dates are not required.

Select your entries for the details column from the following list: Balance b/f, Office equipment, Office expenses, Sales returns, Suspense, Vehicle expenses.

Office expenses

Details	Amount £	Details	Amount £

Office equipment

Details	Amount £	Details	Amount £

Sales returns

Details	Amount £	Details	Amount £

Suspense

Details	Amount £	Details	Amount £
Balance b/f	645		

Vehicle expenses

Details	Amount £	Details	Amount £

6.7 The trial balance of Quaver Music included a suspense account. All the bookkeeping errors have now been traced and the journal entries are shown below.

Account name	Debit	Credit
Sales	99	
Suspense		99
Suspense	1,612	
VAT		1,612
Bank interest paid	52	
Bank charges		52

Post the journal entries to the general ledger accounts on the next page. Dates are not required.

Select your entries for the details column from: Bank charges, Bank interest paid, Sales, Suspense.

Sales

Details	Amount £	Details	Amount £

VAT

Details	Amount £	Details	Amount £

Bank interest paid

Details	Amount £	Details	Amount £

Bank charges

Details	Amount £	Details	Amount £

Suspense

Details	Amount £	Details	Amount £
		Balance b/f	1,513

6.8   On 30 June 20-9 Khela Krafts extracted an initial trial balance which did not balance, and a suspense account was opened. On 1 July journal entries were prepared to correct the errors that had been found, and to clear the suspense account. The list of balances in the initial trial balance, and the journal entries to correct the errors, are shown below and on the next page.

As the accounts assistant at Khela Krafts, you are to redraft the trial balance by placing the figures in the debit or credit column. You should take into account the journal entries (on the next page) which will clear the suspense account.

Account name	Balances extracted on 30 June 20-9 £	Balances at 1 July 20-9	
		Debit £	Credit £
Inventory	8,692		
Sales ledger control	12,347		
Petty cash	84		
Capital	15,287		
Loan from bank	8,625		
VAT owing to HM Revenue & Customs	2,733		
Purchases ledger control	8,421		
Bank (cash at bank)	1,596		
Sales	77,364		
Sales returns	2,913		
Purchases	40,467		
Purchases returns	872		
Wages	20,644		
Advertising	2,397		
Insurance	1,849		
Heating and lighting	1,066		
Rent and rates	3,862		
Vehicle expenses	2,035		
Vehicles	15,400		
Suspense account (credit balance)	50		
Totals			

Journal entries

Account name	Debit £	Credit £
Suspense	490	
Purchases returns		490

Account name	Debit £	Credit £
Suspense	320	
Vehicle expenses		320
Vehicle expenses	230	
Suspense		230

Account name	Debit £	Credit £
Advertising	530	
Suspense		530

Answers to chapter activities

1 Payment methods

1.1 (a) Employee wages

(c) A petty cash system

1.2 (b) Cheque

1.3

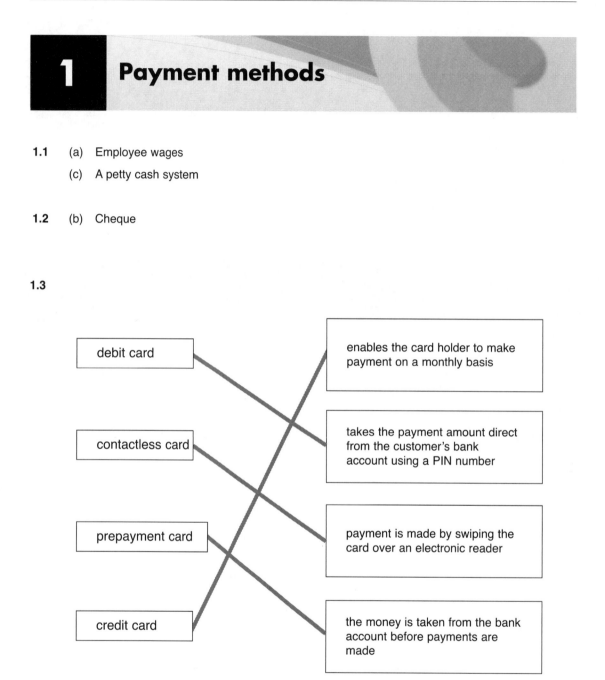

debit card	enables the card holder to make payment on a monthly basis
contactless card	takes the payment amount direct from the customer's bank account using a PIN number
prepayment card	payment is made by swiping the card over an electronic reader
credit card	the money is taken from the bank account before payments are made

1.4 **(a)**, **(c)** and **(d)** are false; **(b)** is true

1.5 A **standing order** is set up by the **payer's bank** and used to make regular electronic payments for the same amount through the banking system.

A **direct debit** on the other hand enables **variable amounts** to be taken from the payer's account and the payments are deducted by the **receiver's bank**.

1.6

			Option number
	(a)	Paying rent for the office at a fixed amount of £750 a month	6
	(b)	Paying insurance premium of £2,000 which increases every year	4
	(c)	Buying office furniture for £1,200 from a local superstore	3
	(d)	Paying solicitors fees of £500 plus VAT in connection with lease	5
	(e)	Buying a travel card for £30 at the local railway station	1

1.7 **(a)** Error 1: The year date is missing

Error 2: The amount in words and figures is different

Error 3: The cheque has not been signed by the issuer

(b) (b) Contact T Witt Trading Ltd and ask for a new cheque to be issued

2   Payment methods and the bank account balance

2.1 (a) The solvency of the business

(d) Keeping bank charges to a minimum

(e) Keeping interest payable on overdrafts to a minimum

2.2 (a) Keeping the bank account in credit whenever possible

(c) Encouraging customers to pay accounts due by Faster Payment

(e) Paying the business insurance costs by direct debit rather than in a lump sum at the beginning of the period of insurance

2.3 (a) Debit
(b) Credit
(c) Credit
(d) Debit

2.4 (a) Faster Payment
(c) CHAPS
(d) Direct debit

2.5 (a) Debit card
(d) Credit card

2.6

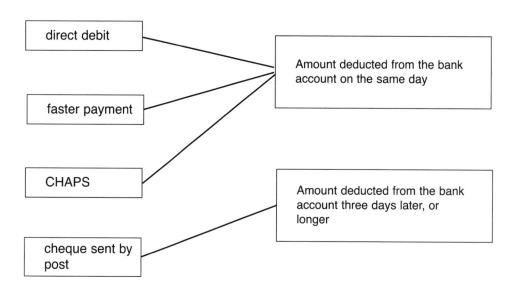

2.7 (b) Pay the invoice so that it reaches the supplier's bank as late as possible within the 30 days limit

3   Bank reconciliation statements

3.1 (c) Automated transfers from customers

3.2 (a) £150 debit

3.3 (a) and (c) true; (b) and (d) false

3.4 It is important to reconcile the cash book to the **bank statement** on a **regular** basis.

The bank statement provides an **independent** accounting record and helps to prevent **fraud**.

It also highlights any **timing** differences and explains why there is a **discrepancy** between the bank statement balance and the **cash book** balance.

3.5 **(a)**

CASH BOOK

Date 20-4	Details	Bank £	Date 20-4	Cheque	Details number	Bank £
1 Jun	Balance b/f	1,830	3 Jun	784343	Gladysz & Co	412
5 Jun	P Parker	1,525	3 Jun	784344	Daley Ltd	697
10 Jun	Dunlevy Ltd	2,607	3 Jun	784345	Ward & Lamb	1,922
25 Jun	Corline Traders	1,433	12 Jun	784346	Hendrie Stores	692
28 Jun	Moss & Co	786	12 Jun	784347	McCabes	1,181
18 Jun	Watson Ltd	2,109	12 Jun	784348	Rehman Ltd	594
			24 Jun		First Electric	112
			29 Jun	784349	Hannaford & Co	764
			25 Jun		Bank charges	45
			30 Jun		Balance c/d	3,871
		10,290				10,290
1 Jul	Balance b/d	3,871				

(b)

Bank reconciliation statement	£
Balance as per bank statement	3,108
Add	
Corline Traders	1,433
Moss & Co	786
Total to add	2,219
Less	
Hendrie Stores	692
Hannaford & Co	764
Total to subtract	1,456
Balance as per cash book	3,871

3.6 The bank **reconciliation** explains any difference between the balance in the **cash book** and the balance at the **bank**.

It highlights any **errors** and **timing differences**.

Access to bank records should be restricted to **authorised** employees to safeguard the **security** of payments and receipts.

4 Using control accounts

4.1 (b) £25,684

4.2 (c) £11,736

4.3 (d) £3,289 credit

4.4 **(a)** **Sales ledger control account**

Details	Amount £	Debit	Credit
Balance owing from credit customers at 1 July	7,298	✔	
Money received from credit customers	6,450		✔
Discounts allowed	75		✔
Goods sold to credit customers	14,774	✔	
Goods returned by credit customers	501		✔
Journal credit to correct an error	89		✔

(b) **Purchases ledger control account**

Details	Amount £	Debit	Credit
Balance owing to credit suppliers at 1 July	2,299		✔
Money paid to credit suppliers	2,276	✔	
Discounts received	23	✔	
Goods purchased from credit suppliers	5,113		✔
Goods returned to credit suppliers	108	✔	

(c) (c) Debit balance of £9,061

(d) (a) is false; (b) and (c) are true.

4.5 **(a)**

Details	Amount £	Debit	Credit
Balance of credit suppliers at 1 June	35,106		✔
Purchases from credit suppliers	20,354		✔
Payments made to credit suppliers	19,062	✔	
Discounts received	289	✔	
Goods returned to credit suppliers	1,374	✔	

(b) (b) Cr £34,735

(c)

	£
Balance on purchases ledger control account at 1 July	34,735
Total of the purchases ledger balances at 1 July	34,442
Difference	293

(d) (b) A credit note was not entered in the purchases ledger control account

4.6 **(a)**

Details	Amount £	Debit	Credit
Balance of credit customers at 1 April	18,392	✔	
Goods sold to credit customers	6,874	✔	
Money received from credit customers	8,937		✔
Discounts allowed	154		✔
Goods returned by credit customers	529		✔

(b) (c) Dr £15,646

(c)

	£
Balance on sales ledger control account at 1 May	15,646
Total of the sales ledger balances at 1 May	16,231
Difference	585

(d) (a) An invoice was entered twice in the sales ledger

(e) (a) and (d) are true

4.7   (a)

VAT control account

Details	Amount £	Details	Amount £
Purchases	7,000	Sales	13,760
Sales returns	448	Purchases returns	328
Discounts allowed	120	Cash sales	568

(b)   No

4.8   (a)

VAT control account

Details	Amount £	Details	Amount £
Purchases	9,080	Balance b/f	9,804
Sales returns	368	Sales	14,800
Petty cash	17	Purchases returns	248
Irrecoverable debts	108	Cash sales	376
Computer equipment	575		
Bank	9,804		

(b)   Yes

(c)   All statements are true.

4.9 (a)

VAT control account

Details	Amount £	Details	Amount £
Sales returns	280	Balance b/f	6,536
Purchases	9,800	Sales	17,080
Petty cash	9	Purchases returns	760
Irrecoverable debts	82	Discounts received	120
Studio equipment	400	Sales	192
Bank	6,536		

(b) Yes

(c) (a) and (b) are true; (c) is false.

5 The journal

5.1 (b) Payroll transactions

5.2

Date 20-4	Details	Reference	Dr £	Cr £
1 Feb	Vehicle	GL	6,500	
	Fixtures and fittings	GL	2,800	
	Inventory	GL	4,100	
	Cash	CB	150	
	Bank	CB	1,250	
	Loan from uncle	GL		5,000
	Capital	GL		9,800
			14,800	14,800
	Journal entries to record the opening entries of the new business.			

5.3   **(a)**

Account name		Debit £	Credit £
Irrecoverable debts		560	
Value Added Tax		112	
Sales ledger control			672

(b)

Account name	Amount £	Debit	Credit
Sales ledger control	14,275	✔	
Purchases ledger control	7,392		✔
Inventory	4,107	✔	
Office equipment	10,400	✔	
Cash at bank	2,822	✔	
Rent and rates	4,086	✔	
Miscellaneous expenses	794	✔	
Wages	2,397	✔	
Loan from bank	6,250		✔
Capital	25,239		✔
Journal entries to record the opening entries of the new business			

5.4 **Journal to record the wages expense**

Account name	Debit £	Credit £
Wages expense	24,489	
Wages control		24,489

Journal to record the HM Revenue & Customs liability

Account name	Debit £	Credit £
Wages control	4,580	
HM Revenue & Customs		4,580

Journal to record the net wages paid to employees

Account name	Debit £	Credit £
Wages control	17,845	
Bank		17,845

Tutorial note: £24,489 − £2,510 − £1,105 − £965 − £1,032 − £1,032 = £17,845

Journal to record the pension fund liability

Account name	Debit £	Credit £
Wages control	2,064	
Pension fund		2,064

5.5 (b), (c), (e) and (f)

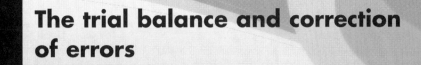

6 The trial balance and correction of errors

6.1 **(a)** Principle

(b) Commission

(c) Original entry

(d) Compensating

(e) Reversal of entries

(f) Omission

6.2

	Debit		**Credit**	
(d)	Telephone expenses	£250	Bank	£250
	Telephone expenses	£250	Bank	£250

6.3 **(a)**

Account name	Debit £	Credit £
Suspense		2,825

(b) (c), (d) and (f) will cause an imbalance; (a), (b) and (e) will not.

6.4 **(a)** **Journal to remove the incorrect entry**

Account name	Debit £	Credit £
Purchases ledger control	2,120	

Journal to record the correct entry

Account name	Debit £	Credit £
Purchases ledger control		2,544

Journal to remove the suspense account balance

Account name	Debit £	Credit £
Suspense	424	

(b) **Journal to remove the incorrect entry**

Account name	Debit £	Credit £
Rent	525	
Bank		525

Journal to record the correct entry

Account name	Debit £	Credit £
Rent	525	
Bank		525

6.5   **(a)**

Account name	Debit £	Credit £
Bank	690	
Rates		690

(b)

Account name	Debit £	Credit £
Rates	609	
Bank		609

6.6

Office expenses

Details	Amount £	Details	Amount £
Office equipment	180		

Office equipment

Details	Amount £	Details	Amount £
		Office expenses	180

Sales returns

Details	Amount £	Details	Amount £
Suspense	295		

Suspense

Details	Amount £	Details	Amount £
Balance b/f	645	Sales returns	295
		Vehicle expenses	350

Vehicle expenses

Details	Amount £	Details	Amount £
Suspense	350		

6.7

Sales

Details	Amount £	Details	Amount £
Suspense	99		

VAT

Details	Amount £	Details	Amount £
		Suspense	1,612

Bank interest paid

Details	Amount £	Details	Amount £
Bank charges	52		

Bank charges

Details	Amount £	Details	Amount £
		Bank interest paid	52

Suspense

Details	Amount £	Details	Amount £
VAT	1,612	Balance b/f	1,513
		Sales	99

6.8

Account name	Balances extracted on 30 June 20-9 £	Balances at 1 July 20-9 Debit £	Credit £
Inventory	8,692	8,692	
Sales ledger control	12,347	12,347	
Petty cash	84	84	
Capital	15,287		15,287
Loan from bank	8,625		8,625
VAT owing to HM Revenue & Customs	2,733		2,733
Purchases ledger control	8,421		8,421
Bank (cash at bank)	1,596	1,596	
Sales	77,364		77,364
Sales returns	2,913	2,913	
Purchases	40,467	40,467	
Purchases returns	872		1,362
Wages	20,644	20,644	
Advertising	2,397	2,927	
Insurance	1,849	1,849	
Heating and lighting	1,066	1,066	
Rent and rates	3,862	3,862	
Vehicle expenses	2,035	1,945	
Vehicles	15,400	15,400	
Suspense account (credit balance)	50	–	–
Totals		113,792	113,792

Practice
assessment 1

Complete all 10 tasks.

Each task is independent. You will not need to refer to your answers in previous tasks. Where the date is relevant, it is given in the task data.

The tasks in this assessment are set in different business situations where the following apply:

- All businesses use a manual bookkeeping system.

- Double-entry takes place in the general ledger. Individual accounts of trade receivables and trade payables are kept in the sales and purchases ledgers as subsidiary accounts.

- The cash book and petty cash book should be treated as part of the double-entry system unless the task instructions state otherwise.

- The VAT rate is 20%.

Task 1

(a)   There are various methods of payment available to bank account holders.

You are to match each of the payment needs listed in the boxes on the left with the most appropriate payment method listed on the right. In each case draw a line between the boxes indicating your choice.

Tristan Instruments Ltd has to make regular equal monthly payments of £100 for a loan raised from a finance company	credit card
Lily Designs does not like the risks of having to use cash for small purchases and needs a safer method of paying for low value items	direct debit
Boris Instruments Ltd has employed a new travelling salesman who needs to pay for expenses on his business trips	bank draft
Wheatley & Co have taken out insurance which involves making payments which will increase during the course of the year	standing order
James Rich is buying a Ferrari for £175,000 as a company car but the garage needs a form of payment that cannot be stopped by the buyer	contactless debit card

(b)

Managing the level of funds on a bank account requires careful use of payment methods because they vary in the length of time they take to deduct the funds from the account.

Identify the time lag involved in using the four methods shown on the left below below and draw a line between the relevant box on the left and the appropriate box on the right. Note that not all the boxes on the right are relevant.

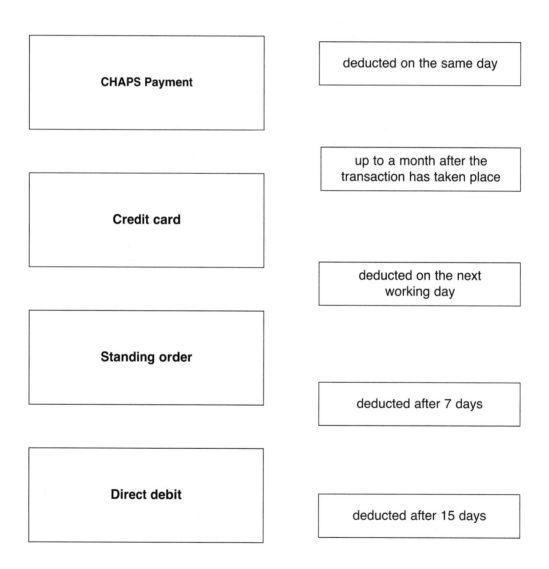

| CHAPS Payment | deducted on the same day |

| Credit card | up to a month after the transaction has taken place |

| Standing order | deducted on the next working day |

| | deducted after 7 days |

| Direct debit | deducted after 15 days |

(c)   It is important to understand the effects of errors in a bookkeeping system.

Show which of the errors below will cause an imbalance in the trial balance by placing a tick in the appropriate column for each error.

Error	Will cause an imbalance in the trial balance	Will not cause an imbalance in the trial balance
(a) Commission received of £150 has been credited to rent received account		
(b) Sales returns of £225 have been credited to sales account		
(c) A bank payment for vehicle repairs has been recorded in the cash book only		
(d) The balance of sales account has been calculated incorrectly		

(d)   Classify the following errors:

Error	Error of omission	Error of original entry	Error of commission
(a) Discounts received of £72 has been recorded in the discounts received account as £27			
(b) A bank payment to a credit supplier has not been entered in the cash book or the purchases ledger control account			
(c) A sales invoice for £340 for Playwell Ltd has been debited to the account of Playtime Ltd			

(e)   The writing off of irrecoverable debts from the bookkeeping system is recorded in the journal.

State **one** other transaction that is recorded in the journal:

Choose from the following list: Correction of errors, Faster payments to suppliers, Prompt payment discounts allowed, Sale of goods on credit to customers.

Task 2

Payroll transactions are recorded using a wages control account.

The wages expense for July is £40,827. Other payroll information for the month is shown below:	
• Income tax	£4,780
• Employer's National Insurance	£3,840
• Employees' National Insurance	£2,860
• Employer's pension contribution	£1,740
• Employees' pension contribution	£1,740

Show the journal entries needed to record:
• the HM Revenue & Customs liability
• the net wages paid to employees
• the pension fund liability

Do not enter a zero in unused debit or credit column cells.

Select your account names from the following list: Bank, Employees' National Insurance, Employer's National Insurance, HM Revenue & Customs, Income tax, Net wages, Pension fund, Wages control, Wages expense.

Journal to record the HM Revenue & Customs liability

Account name	Debit £	Credit £

Journal to record the net wages paid to employees

Account name	Debit £	Credit £

Journal to record the pension fund liability

Account name	Debit £	Credit £

Task 3

This is a customer's account in the sales ledger:

Froggatt Limited

Date	Details	Amount	Date	Details	Amount
20-4		£	20-4		£
1 Jul	Balance b/f	1,038	4 Jul	Credit note 67	78
15 Jul	Invoice 320	288	18 Jul	Credit note 75	144

This customer has now ceased trading owing the amount outstanding, which includes VAT.

(a)   Record the journal entries needed in the general ledger to write off the net amount and the VAT.

Do not enter a zero in unused debit or credit column cells.

Select your account names from the following list: Froggatt Limited, Irrecoverable debts, Purchases, Purchases ledger control, Sales, Sales ledger control, VAT control.

Journal

Account name	Debit £	Credit £

(b)   A new business has been started and a new set of accounts is to be opened.

A partially completed journal to record the opening entries is shown below.

Complete the journal by entering each amount in either the debit or credit column.

Journal

Account name	Amount £	Debit £	Credit £
Fixtures and fittings	7,500		
Bank overdraft	2,150		
Capital	10,000		
Sales ledger control	4,650		

Task 4

(a)   This is a summary of transactions to be recorded in the VAT control account in July.

Show whether each transaction will be a debit or credit entry in the VAT control account.

Transaction	Amount £	Debit	Credit
VAT owing to HM Revenue & Customs at 1 July	1,585		
VAT total in the sales day book	2,627		
VAT total in the purchases day book	1,345		
VAT total in the purchases returns day book	286		
VAT total in the discounts received day book	154		
VAT total in the cash book for cash sales	728		
VAT total in the petty cash book for expenses	22		
VAT payment made to HM Revenue & Customs	1,585		

(b)   At the end of August the VAT control account has debit entries amounting to £3,422 and credit entries amounting to £6,155.

The following transactions have not yet been recorded in the VAT control account:

•   VAT total of £310 in the sales returns day book

•   VAT of £115 on an irrecoverable debt written off

What will be the balance brought down on the VAT control account after the transactions above have been recorded?

Amount £	Debit	Credit

Task 5

These are the accounts in the purchases ledger at 1 September.

Brocken Ltd

Details	Amount £	Details	Amount £
		Balance b/f	7,328

Annan plc

Details	Amount £	Details	Amount £
		Balance b/f	4,111

Elend & Sons

Details	Amount £	Details	Amount £
Balance b/f	384		

White and Hart

Details	Amount £	Details	Amount £
		Balance b/f	5,176

(a) What is the total of the balances in the purchases ledger on 1 September?

£ [   ]

(b) The balance of the purchases ledger control account on 1 September is £15,646.

What is the difference between the balance of the purchases ledger control account and the total of the balances of the purchases ledger you calculated in (a)?

£ [   ]

(c)   Which **two** of the reasons below could explain the difference you calculated in (b)?

Reasons	
(a) Goods bought were entered twice in a supplier's account in the purchases ledger	
(b) Goods returned were not entered in the purchases ledger control account	
(c) Goods returned were entered twice in a supplier's account in the purchases ledger	
(d) Discounts received were not entered in the purchases ledger control account	
(e) A bank payment to a supplier was entered into the wrong supplier's account in the purchases ledger	
(f) A bank payment to a supplier was entered twice in the purchases ledger control account	

(d)   This is a summary of transactions with credit customers during September.

Transactions	Amount £
Balance due at 1 September	25,614
Goods sold	14,385
Bank payments received	19,317
Goods returned	2,065

Record these transactions in the sales ledger control account and show the balance carried down.

Select your entries for the details column from the following list: Balance b/d, Balance c/d, Bank, Discounts allowed, Discounts received, Purchases, Purchases returns, Sales, Sales returns.

Sales ledger control

Details	Amount £	Details	Amount £
Total		Total	

Task 6

The bank statement and cash book for June are shown below.

Check the bank statement against the cash book and enter:

*   any transactions into the cash book as needed
*   the cash book balance carried down at 30 June and brought down at 1 July

BANK STATEMENT				
Date	**Details**	**Paid out**	**Paid in**	**Balance**
20-4		£	£	£
01 Jun	Balance b/f			1,487 C
04 Jun	Cheque 114117	395		1,092 C
05 Jun	Cheque 114118	1,310		218 D
05 Jun	BACS credit: Cottle Ltd		4,806	4,588 C
18 Jun	Cheque 114119	2,218		2,370 C
20 Jun	Direct debit: Wyvern Council	235		2,135 C
21 Jun	BACS credit: Bayer Ltd		1,095	3,230 C
21 Jun	BACS credit: Allen plc		2,786	6,016 C
22 Jun	Direct debit: JA Finance	592		5,424 C
22 Jun	Cheque 114121	1,427		3,997 C
24 Jun	Counter credit		2,108	6,105 C
28 Jun	Bank charges	45		6,060 C
D = Debit C = Credit				

CASH BOOK

Date 20-4	Details	Bank £	Date 20-4	Cheque number	Details	Bank £
1 Jun	Balance b/f	1,487	1 Jun	114117	Hendric & Co	395
4 Jun	Cottle Ltd	4,806	1 Jun	114118	Harrup & Noyes	1,310
20 Jun	W Waugh	2,108	10 Jun	114119	Farr Ltd	2,218
24 Jun	Pardo Ltd	1,746	18 Jun	114120	Bradnock Trading	1,036
24 Jun	Torre & Co	542	18 Jun	114121	Paxtons	1,427
			18 Jun	114122	Filiaps Ltd	798
			20 Jun		Wyvern Council	235

Select your entries for the details column from the following list: Allen plc, Balance b/d, Balance c/d, Bank charges, Bayer Ltd, Bradnock Trading, Closing balance, Cottle Ltd, Farr Ltd, Filiaps Ltd, Harrup & Noyes, Hendric & Co, JA Finance, Opening balance, Pardo Ltd, Paxtons, Torre & Co, W Waugh, Wyvern Council.

Task 7

Below is the bank statement for September.

BANK STATEMENT				
Date 20-4	Details	Paid out £	Paid in £	Balance £
1 Sep	Balance b/f			94 D
2 Sep	Counter credit		2,863	2,769 C
7 Sep	Cheque 145002	168		2,601 C
11 Sep	Cheque 145003	780		1,821 C
12 Sep	Counter credit		563	2,384 C
17 Sep	Cheque 145004	129		2,255 C
19 Sep	BACS: J Jones Ltd		472	2,727 C
22 Sep	Direct Debit: Wyvern Council	609		2,118 C
24 Sep	Counter credit		439	2,557 C
25 Sep	Bank charges	66		2,491 C

D = Debt   C = Credit

The cash book as at 30 September is shown below.

Date 20-4	Details	Bank £	Date 20-4	Cheque number	Details	Bank £
1 Sep	Balance b/f	2,769	5 Sep	145002	Farr Ltd	168
12 Sep	Torre & Co	563	8 Sep	145003	Paxtons	780
19 Sep	BACS J Jones	472	12 Sep	145004	Donfar & Co	129
24 Sep	LLR Ltd	439	16 Sep	145005	O Borne	760
29 Sep	W Waugh	946	22 Sep	DD	Wyvern CC	609
30 Sep	Preston Ltd	247	23 Sep	BACS	Filiaps	1,055
			25 Sep		Bank charges	66

The cash book and bank reconciliation statement for September have not yet been finalised.

(a)   Identify the **four** transactions that are included in the cash book but missing from the bank statement and complete the bank reconciliation statement below as at 30 September.

Do not enter minus signs or brackets in this task.

Select your entries from the following list:
Bank charges, O Borne, Donfar & Co, Farr Ltd, Filiaps, J Jones, LLR Ltd, Paxtons, Preston Ltd, Torre & Co, W Waugh, Wyvern CC.

Bank reconciliation statement	£
Balance as per bank statement	
Add	
Total to add	
Less	
Total to subtract	
Balance as per cash book	

(b)   Refer to the cash book on the previous page and check that the bank statement has been correctly reconciled by calculating:

• the balance carried down

• the total of each of the bank columns after the balance carried down has been recorded

Balance carried down £	Bank column totals £

Task 8

A suspense account has been opened with a balance of £1,000.

The error has been identified as an entry made in the general ledger from the incorrect addition of the total column in the purchases day book shown below.

Purchases day book

Date 20-4	Details	Invoice number	Total £	VAT £	Net £
30 Jun	Maldanado and Co	5916	3,600	600	3,000
30 Jun	Murray Ltd	M/3421	1,680	280	1,400
30 Jun	Bromfield Supplies	B8624	480	80	400
	Totals		4,760	960	4,800

(a) Record the journal entries needed to:
- remove the incorrect entry
- record the correct entry
- remove the suspense account balance

Do not enter a zero in unused debit or credit column cells.

Select your account name from the following list: Bromfield Supplies, Maldanado and Co, Murray Ltd, Purchases, Purchases day book, Purchases ledger control, Purchases returns, Purchases returns day book, Sales, Sales day book, Sales ledger control, Sales returns, Sales returns day book, Suspense, Value Added Tax.

Journal to remove the incorrect entry

Account name	Debit £	Credit £

Journal to record the correct entry

Account name	Debit £	Credit £

Journal to remove the suspense account balance

Account name	Debit £	Credit £

(b) Another error has been found in the general ledger. Entries to record a bank receipt of £220 for commission received have been reversed.

Record the journal entries to:

•   remove the incorrect entry

•   record the correct entry

Do not enter a zero in unused debit or credit column cells.

Select your account names from the following list: Bank, Cash, Commission received, Purchases, Purchases ledger control, Sales, Sales ledger control, Suspense, VAT.

Journal to remove the incorrect entries

Account name	Debit £	Credit £

Journal to record the correct entries

Account name	Debit £	Credit £

Task 9

The journal entries below have been prepared to correct an error.

Journal

Account name	Debit £	Credit £
Vehicles	10,560	
Suspense		10,560
Suspense	10,650	
Vehicles		10,650

Record the journal entries in the general ledger accounts below and show the balance carried down in the vehicles account.

Select your entries for the details column from the following list: Balance b/d, Balance c/d, Bank, Suspense, Vehicles.

Vehicles

Details	Amount £	Details	Amount £
Balance b/f	28,240		
Bank	12,385		

Suspense

Details	Amount £	Details	Amount £
		Balance b/f	90

Task 10

On 30 June a trial balance was extracted and did not balance. The debit column totalled £146,852 and the credit column totalled £145,902.

(a) What entry is needed in the suspense account to balance the trial balance?

Do not enter a zero in the unused column cell.

Account name	Debit £	Credit £
Suspense		

(b) The journal entries to correct all the bookkeeping errors, and a list of balances as they appear in the trial balance, are shown below.

Journal

Account name	Debit £	Credit £
Suspense	1,450	
Rent paid		1,450
Purchases	500	
Suspense		500
Office expenses	125	
Bank		125
Office expenses	125	
Bank		125

Complete the table below to show:
- the balance of each account after the journal entries have been recorded
- whether each balance will be a debit or credit entry in the trial balance

List of balances

Account name	Original balance £	New balance £	Debit in trial balance	Credit in trial balance
Rent paid	7,055			
Purchases	65,032			
Office expenses	9,536			
Bank (overdraft)	2,088			

(c) On 31 July a partially prepared trial balance had debit balances totalling £177,338 and credit balances totalling £183,379. The accounts below have not yet been entered into the trial balance.

Complete the table below to show whether each balance will be a debit or credit entry in the trial balance.

Account name	Balance £	Debit in trial balance	Credit in trial balance
Purchases returns	1,247		
Petty cash	68		
Drawings	7,220		

(d) What will be the totals of each column of the trial balance after the balances in (c) have been entered?

Account name	Debit £	Credit £
Totals		

Practice assessment 2

Complete all 10 tasks.

Each task is independent. You will not need to refer to your answers in previous tasks. Where the date is relevant, it is given in the task data.

The tasks in this assessment are set in different business situations where the following apply:

- All businesses use a manual bookkeeping system.

- Double-entry takes place in the general ledger. Individual accounts of trade receivables and trade payables are kept in the sales and purchases ledgers as subsidiary accounts.

- The cash book and petty cash book should be treated as part of the double-entry system unless the task instructions state otherwise.

- The VAT rate is 20%.

Task 1

(a)   There are various methods of payment available to bank account holders.

You are to match each of the payment needs listed in the boxes on the left with the most appropriate payment method listed on the right. In each case draw a line between the boxes indicating your choice.

Heidi Hairdressing wants to make a £50 contribution to a local charity but prefers to send it by post with a covering letter as that is a more personal way of giving	direct BACS credit
Martin's Properties Ltd has used a self-employed plumber who has asked that £185 is paid direct to his bank account within seven days	cheque
Lola Piercings has just started business and needs a payment card for business expenses which will not result in her running up any debts	Faster Payment
Foxey & Co has bought a new small office and needs to transfer £225,000 electronically to a firm of solicitors in order to complete the purchase	debit card
Cool Shades is a shop that has recently opened and the owner wants to pay her staff by electronic transfer with variable amounts that differ each month	CHAPS

(b) Max James is setting up a new business and wants to know how long it will take for money to be added to the new business bank account when he receives payments. He wants to keep as much money on the account as he can at any one time.

Identify the time lag involved in using the five payment methods shown on the left below and draw a line between the relevant box on the left and the appropriate box on the right.

Cash paid into the bank	
	added to the account on the same day that it is processed by the payer's bank
Cheque	
	added to the account on the next working day or later after payment has been made by the payer
Debit card	
	added to the account immediately when paid in at the bank over the counter
Faster payment	
	added to the account when paid in at the bank over the counter – but the money cannot be withdrawn immediately
Bankers draft	

(c)   It is important to understand the effects of errors in a bookkeeping system.

Show which of the errors below will cause an imbalance in the trial balance by placing a tick in the appropriate column for each error.

Error	Will cause an imbalance in the trial balance	Will not cause an imbalance in the trial balance
(a) Recording a bank payment for heat and light on the debit side of both the bank and heat and light account		
(b) Incorrectly calculating the balance on the rent account		
(c) Recording a bank payment to a creditor in the bank account and purchases ledger only		
(d) Recording a bank payment of £470 for motor repairs as £4,700 in both accounts		

(d)   Classify the following errors:

Error	Reversal of entries	Error of original entry	Error of principle
(a) Recording a payment for motor repairs in the motor vehicles account			
(b) Recording a sales credit note on the debit side of the sales ledger control account and the credit side of the sales returns account			
(c) Recording a bank payment for a telephone bill as £249 in both accounts when the actual bill was for £294			

(e)   State **one** transaction that is recorded in the journal:

Choose from the following list: Bank payments to suppliers, Opening entries for a new business, Petty cash payments, Prompt payment discounts received.

Task 2

Payroll transactions are recorded using a wages control account.

The wages expense for May is £17,966. Other payroll information for the month is shown below:	
• Employer's National Insurance	£1,730
• Employees' National Insurance	£1,620
• Income tax	£1,808

In addition there are voluntary deductions for 10 employees who each pay £20 a month for trade union fees.

Show the journal entries needed to record:
- the HM Revenue & Customs liability
- the net wages paid to employees
- trade union liability

Do not enter a zero in unused debit or credit column cells.

Select your account names from the following list: Bank, Employees' NI, Employer's NI, HM Revenue & Customs, Income tax, Net wages, Trade union, Wages control, Wages expense.

Journal to record the HM Revenue & Customs liability

Account name	Debit £	Credit £

Journal to record the net wages paid to employees

Account name	Debit £	Credit £

Journal to record the trade union liability

Account name	Debit £	Credit £

Task 3

This is a customer's account in the sales ledger:

Brant Limited

Date	Details	Amount	Date	Details	Amount
20-4		£	20-4		£
1 June	Balance b/f	1,230	3 June	Credit note 48	72
18 June	Invoice 562	514	12 June	Credit note 52	112

This customer has now ceased trading owing the amount outstanding, which includes VAT.

(a) Record the journal entries needed in the general ledger to write off the net amount and the VAT.

Do not enter a zero in unused debit or credit column cells.

Select your account names from the following list: Brant Limited, Irrecoverable debts, Purchases, Purchases ledger control, Sales, Sales ledger control, VAT control.

Journal

Account name	Debit £	Credit £

(b) A new business has been started and a new set of accounts is to be opened.

A partially completed journal to record the opening entries is shown below.

Complete the journal by entering each amount in either the debit or credit column.

Journal

Account name	Amount £	Debit £	Credit £
Office equipment	5,650		
Cash at bank	850		
Capital	4,000		
Loan from bank	2,500		

Task 4

(a) This is a summary of transactions to be recorded in the VAT control account in June.

Show whether each transaction will be a debit or credit entry in the VAT control account.

Transaction	Amount £	Debit	Credit
VAT refund due from HM Revenue & Customs at 1 June	1,021		
VAT total in the sales day book	1,854		
VAT total in the purchases day book	1,397		
VAT total in the sales returns day book	159		
VAT total in the discounts allowed day book	76		
VAT total in the cash book for cash sales	528		
VAT total in the petty cash book for expenses	36		
VAT receipt from HM Revenue & Customs	1,021		

(b) At the end of July the VAT control account has debit entries amounting to £2,878 and credit entries amounting to £2,915.

The following transactions have not yet been recorded in the VAT control account:

- VAT total of £77 in the discounts received day book
- VAT of £198 on an irrecoverable debt written off

What will be the balance brought down on the VAT control account after the transactions above have been recorded?

Amount £	Debit	Credit

Task 5

These are the accounts in the sales ledger at 1 August.

Satar Ltd

Details	Amount £	Details	Amount £
Balance b/f	5,392		

Simmonds plc

Details	Amount £	Details	Amount £
Balance b/f	4,186		

Sidhu & Sons

Details	Amount £	Details	Amount £
Balance b/f	2,573		

Rani and Rani

Details	Amount £	Details	Amount £
		Balance b/f	225

(a)   What is the total of the balances in the sales ledger on 1 August?

£ [   ]

(b)   The balance of the sales ledger control account on 1 August is £12,798.

What is the difference between the balance of the sales ledger control account and the total of the balances of the sales ledger you calculated in (a)?

£ [   ]

(c)   Which **two** of the reasons below could explain the difference you calculated in (b)?

Reasons	
(a) Goods sold have not been entered in the customers' accounts in the sales ledger	
(b) Goods returned have been entered twice in the sales ledger control account	
(c) A bank receipt was not entered in a customer's account in the sales ledger	
(d) Goods returned have been entered in the wrong customer's account in the sales ledger	
(e) Discounts allowed have not been entered in the customers' accounts in the sales ledger	
(f) Irrecoverable debts written off have not been entered in the sales ledger control account	

(d)   This is a summary of transactions with credit suppliers during August.

Transactions	Amount £
Balance owing at 1 August	18,976
Goods purchased	10,325
Bank payments made	15,147
Goods returned	1,034

Record these transactions in the purchases ledger control account and show the balance carried down.

Select your entries for the details column from the following list: Balance b/d, Balance c/d, Bank, Discounts allowed, Discounts received, Purchases, Purchases returns, Sales, Sales returns.

Purchases ledger control

Details	Amount £	Details	Amount £
Total		Total	

Task 6

The bank statement and cash book for June are shown below.

Check the bank statement against the cash book and enter:

- any transactions into the cash book as needed
- the cash book balance carried down at 30 June and brought down at 1 July

Bank Statement				
Date	**Details**	**Paid out**	**Paid in**	**Balance**
20-4		£	£	£
04 June	Balance b/f			15,189 C
04 June	Cheque 111042	10,000		5,189 C
04 June	Cheque 111043	1,420		3,769 C
05 June	Cheque 111044	80		3,689 C
06 June	Cheque 111047	2,500		1,189 C
12 June	BACS Credit: Cabot and Co		571	1,760 C
13 June	Cheque 111045	795		965 C
13 June	Direct Debit: LMBC	150		815 C
20 June	Direct Debit: Insurance Direct	850		35 D
23 June	Bank charges	88		123 D
26 June	Overdraft fee	30		153 D
29 June	Counter credit		175	22 C
D = Debit C = Credit				

Cash book

Date 20-4	Details	Bank £	Date 20-4	Cheque number	Details	Bank £
1 June	Balance b/f	15,189	1 June	111042	Prime kitchens	10,000
16 June	Britten & Bond	175	1 June	111043	Equipdirect	1,420
20 June	Macklin Ltd	950	1 June	111044	Long and Lane	80
21 June	Randle Fitments	300	1 June	111045	BLH Ltd	795
			2 June	111046	MVR Ltd	652
			2 June	111047	Fairfield Ltd	2,500
			13 June	111048	Makin and King	450
			13 June		LMBC	150

Select your entries for the details column from the following list: Balance b/d, Balance c/d, Bank charges, BLH Ltd, Britten & Bond, Cabot and Co, Closing balance, Equipdirect, Fairfield Ltd, Insurance Direct, LMBC, Long and Lane, Macklin Ltd, Makin and King, MVR Ltd, Opening balance, Overdraft fees, Prime Kitchens, Randle Fitments.

Task 7

Below is the bank statement for September.

BANK STATEMENT				
Date **20-4**		**Paid out** £	**Paid in** £	**Balance** £
01 Sep	Balance b/f			252 C
02 Sep	Cheque 112001	1,628		1,376 D
04 Sep	Counter credit		2,307	931 C
08 Sep	Cheque 112003	186		745 C
12 Sep	Cheque 112002	870		125 D
13 Sep	Counter credit		653	528 C
18 Sep	Cheque 112004	219		309 C
20 Sep	BACS Cabot and Co		742	1,051 C
23 Sep	Direct debit: Commercial Prop	600		451 C
25 Sep	Counter credit		349	800 C
26 Sep	Bank charges	48		752 C
D = Debit C =Credit				

The cash book as at 30 September is shown below.

Date 20-4	Details	Bank £	Date 20-4	Cheque number	Details	Bank £
4 Sep	Brownlow	2,307	1 Sep		Balance b/f	1,376
13 Sep	Peer Prints	653	6 Sep	112003	Ace Timber	186
20 Sep	BACS Cabot and Co	742	9 Sep	112002	Fairfield Ltd	870
25 Sep	GTK Ltd	349	13 Sep	112004	BLH Ltd	219
29 Sep	Barber Bates Ltd	469	17 Sep	112005	Bridge Tools	607
30 Sep	Jackson & Co	245	23 Sep	DD	Commercial Prop	600
			24 Sep	112006	Tenon Ltd	1,505
			26 Sep		Bank charges	48

The cash book and bank reconciliation statement for September have not yet been finalised.

(a) Identify the **four** transactions that are included in the cash book but missing from the bank statement and complete the bank reconciliation statement below as at 30 September.

Do not enter minus signs of brackets in this task.

Select your entries from the following list:
Ace Timber, Bank charges, Barber Bates Ltd, BLH Ltd, Bridge Tools, Brownlow, Cabot and Co, Commercial Prop, Fairfield Ltd, GTK Ltd, Jackson & Co, Peer Prints, Tenon Ltd.

Bank reconciliation statement	£
Balance as per bank statement	
Add	
Total to add	
Less	
Total to subtract	
Balance as per cash book	

(b) Refer to the cash book on the previous page and check that the bank statement has been correctly reconciled by calculating:

- the balance carried down

- the total of each of the bank columns after the balance carried down has been recorded

Balance carried down	Bank column totals
£	£

Task 8

A suspense account has been opened with a balance of £100.

The error has been identified as an entry made in the general ledger from the incorrectly totalled VAT column in the sales returns day book shown below.

Sales returns day book

Date 20-4	Details	Invoice number	Total £	VAT £	Net £
30 June	Barber Bates Ltd	367	720	120	600
30 June	GTK Ltd	368	4,320	720	3,600
30 June	Peer Prints	369	960	160	800
	Totals		6,000	1,100	5,000

(a) Record the journal entries needed to:

- remove the incorrect entry
- record the correct entry
- remove the suspense account balance

Do not enter a zero in unused debit or credit column cells.

Select your account name from the following list: Barber Bates Ltd, GTK Ltd, Peer Prints, Purchases, Purchases day book, Purchases ledger control, Purchases returns, Purchases returns day book, Sales, Sales day book, Sales ledger control, Sales returns, Sales returns day book, Suspense, VAT.

Journal to remove the incorrect entry

Account name	Debit £	Credit £

Journal to record the correct entry

Account name	Debit £	Credit £

Journal to remove the suspense account balance

Account name	Debit £	Credit £

(b) Another error has been found in the general ledger. Entries to record a bank payment of £350 for heat and light have been reversed.

Record the journal entries to:

•   remove the incorrect entry

•   record the correct entry

Do not enter a zero in unused debit or credit column cells.

Select your account names from the following list: Bank, Cash, Heat and light, Purchases, Purchases ledger control, Sales, Sales ledger control, Suspense, VAT.

Journal to remove the incorrect entries

Account name	Debit £	Credit £

Journal to record the correct entries

Account name	Debit £	Credit £

Task 9

The journal entries below have been prepared to correct an error.

Journal

Account name	Debit £	Credit £
Rent paid	1,250	
Suspense		1,250
Suspense	1,520	
Rent paid		1,520

Record the journal entries in the general ledger accounts below and show the balance carried down in the rent paid account.

Select your entries for the details column from the following list: Balance b/d, Balance c/d, Bank, Rent paid, Suspense.

Rent paid

Details	Amount £	Details	Amount £
Balance b/f	12,360		
Bank	1,050		

Suspense

Details	Amount £	Details	Amount £
		Balance b/f	270

Task 10

On 30 April a trial balance was extracted and did not balance. The debit column totalled £156,966 and the credit column totalled £155,521.

(a)   What entry is needed in the suspense account to balance the trial balance?

Do not enter a zero in the unused column cell.

Account name	Debit £	Credit £
Suspense		

(b)   The journal entries to correct all the bookkeeping errors, and a list of balances as they appear in the trial balance, are shown below.

Journal

Account name	Debit £	Credit £
Office stationery	355	
Suspense		355
Suspense	1,800	
Rent received		1,800
Telephone	225	
Bank		225
Telephone	225	
Bank		225

Complete the table below to show:
*   the balance of each account after the journal entries have been recorded
*   whether each balance will be a debit or credit entry in the trial balance

List of balances

Account name	Original balance £	New balance £	Debit in trial balance	Credit in trial balance
Office stationery	3,027			
Rent received	8,040			
Telephone	1,285			
Bank (overdraft)	3,261			

(c) On 31 May a partially prepared trial balance had debit balances totalling £153,258 and credit balances totalling £151,504. The accounts below have not yet been entered into the trial balance.

Complete the table below to show whether each balance will be a debit or credit entry in the trial balance.

Account name	Balance £	Debit in trial balance	Credit in trial balance
Sales returns	1,364		
Discounts received	728		
VAT (owing to HM Revenue & Customs)	2,390		

(d) What will be the totals of each column of the trial balance after the balances in (c) have been entered?

Account name	Debit £	Credit £
Totals		

Practice
assessment 3

Complete all 10 tasks.

Each task is independent. You will not need to refer to your answers in previous tasks. Where the date is relevant, it is given in the task data.

The tasks in this assessment are set in different business situations where the following apply:

- All businesses use a manual bookkeeping system.

- Double-entry takes place in the general ledger. Individual accounts of trade receivables and trade payables are kept in the sales and purchases ledgers as subsidiary accounts.

- The cash book and petty cash book should be treated as part of the double-entry system unless the task instructions state otherwise.

- The VAT rate is 20%.

Task 1

(a)   Complete the boxes in the text below by inserting the appropiate payment method from the following list:

standing order

direct debit

debit card

CHAPS

direct credits

Faster Payment

credit card

makes the payment

receives the payment

The system set up by the banks for same day large payments is the [   ] system.

If the amount to be paid electronically is smaller the bank [   ] system should be used.

For repeated electronic payments the banks offer a [   ] which is suitable for situations when the amount and time interval is always the same.

The banks also offer the [   ] system when the amounts and time intervals can vary.

The bank that sets up the payment in this case is the bank that [   ] .

[   ] are used to make variable electronic payments, eg payroll payments.

These are set up by the bank that [   ] .

Plastic cards are also used to make payments. Transactions using a [   ] are deducted from the bank account on the next day and a [   ] allows monthly settlement to be made for the total expenses incurred during that month.

(b) Different types of bank payment can take different periods of time after they have been issued and before they are deducted from the bank account of the business making the payment.

Choose the appropriate deduction periods from the list shown below for the different types of payment set out in the left-hand column of the table.

Enter the correct deduction period in the right-hand column of the table.

same day

three working days later or more

up to a month after the transaction date

Payment method	Deduction from the bank account
cheque	
cash withdrawal from bank	
CHAPS	
credit card	
Faster Payment	

(c) It is important to understand the effects of errors in a bookkeeping system. Show which of the errors below will cause an imbalance in the trial balance by ticking the appropriate column for each error.

Error	Will cause an imbalance in the trial balance	Will not cause an imbalance in the trial balance
(a) A cash purchase has been entered in the cash book but not in the purchases account		
(b) Discounts allowed of £98 have been recorded in the discounts allowed account as £89		
(c) A receipt from a credit customer has not been entered in the cash book or in the sales ledger control account		
(d) A purchase credit note for £296 has been debited to the purchases account and credited to the purchases ledger control account		

(d) Classify the following errors:

Error	Error of principle	Compensating error	Error of commission
(a) The purchase of vehicles for £10,000 has been debited to the vehicle expenses account			
(b) The sales account has been overcast by £10. The purchases account has also been overcast by £10			
(c) A purchase invoice for £235 for Stanway Supplies Ltd has been credited to the account of Stanway Equipment Ltd			

(e) Which **one** of the following best describes the purpose of the journal?

(a) A book of prime entry to record credit sale and credit purchse transactions	
(b) A bookkeeping account in the general ledger to record transactions made in error	
(c) A book of prime entry to record bank receipts and payments	
(d) A book of prime entry to record non-regular transactions	

Task 2

Payroll transactions are recorded using a wages control account.

The wages expense for July is £50,176. Other payroll information for the month is shown below:	
• Income tax	£4,798
• Employees' National Insurance	£2,467
• Employer's National Insurance	£2,694
• Employees' pension contribution	£2,321
• Employer's pension contribution	£1,032

Show the journal entries needed to record:
- the net wages paid to employees
- the HM Revenue & Customs liability
- the pension fund liability

Do not enter a zero in unused debit or credit column cells.

Select your account names from the following list: Bank, Employees' National Insurance, Employer's National Insurance, HM Revenue & Customs, Income tax, Net wages, Pension, Wages control, Wages expense.

Journal to record the net wages paid to employees

Account name	Debit £	Credit £

Journal to record the HM Revenue & Customs liability

Account name	Debit £	Credit £

Journal to record the pension fund liability

Account name	Debit £	Credit £

Task 3

This is a customer's account in the sales ledger:

Toni Campbell

Date	Details	Amount	Date	Details	Amount
20-4		£	20-4		£
1 Dec	Balance b/f	875	5 Dec	Credit note 88	48
3 Dec	Invoice 562	339	10 Dec	Credit note 92	26

This customer has now ceased trading owing the amount outstanding, which includes VAT.

(a)   Record the journal entries needed in the general ledger to write off the net amount and the VAT.

Do not enter a zero in unused debit or credit column cells.

Select your account names from the following list: Toni Campbell, Irrecoverable debts, Purchases, Purchases ledger control, Sales, Sales ledger control, VAT control.

Journal

Account name	Debit £	Credit £

(b)   A new business has been started and a new set of accounts is to be opened.

A partially completed journal to record the opening entries is shown below.

Complete the journal by entering each amount in either the debit or credit column.

Journal

Account name	Amount £	Debit £	Credit £
Capital	10,000		
Bank loan	2,500		
Computer equipment	8,620		
Inventory	3,880		

Task 4

(a)   This is a summary of transactions to be recorded in the VAT control account in November.

Show whether each transaction will be a debit or credit entry in the VAT control account.

Transaction	Amount £	Debit	Credit
VAT owing to HM Revenue & Customs at 1 November	2,735		
VAT total in the sales day book	3,192		
VAT total in the purchases day book	2,085		
VAT total in the purchases returns day book	176		
VAT total in the discounts allowed day book	105		
VAT total in the cash book for cash purchases	85		
VAT on purchase of computers for use in the office	947		
VAT payment made to HM Revenue & Customs	2,735		

(b)   At the end of December the VAT control account has debit entries amounting to £6,022 and credit entries amounting to £8,125.

The following transactions have not yet been recorded in the VAT control account:

- VAT total of £292 in the sales returns day book

- VAT total of £24 in the petty cash book.

What will be the balance brought down on the VAT control account after the transactions above have been recorded?

Amount £	Debit	Credit

Task 5

These are the accounts in the purchases ledger at 1 September.

Akamo Ltd

Details	Amount £	Details	Amount £
		Balance b/f	6,107

Ryton plc

Details	Amount £	Details	Amount £
		Balance b/f	10,245

Murray & Sons

Details	Amount £	Details	Amount £
		Balance b/f	3,097

Baig and Bailey

Details	Amount £	Details	Amount £
Balance b/f	368		

(a)   What is the total of the balances in the purchases ledger on 1 December?

£

(b)   The balance of the purchases ledger control account on 1 December is £19,267.

What is the difference between the balance of the purchases ledger control account and the total of the balances of the purchases ledger you calculated in (a)?

£

(c) Which **two** of the reasons below could explain the difference you calculated in (b)?

Reasons	
(a) Goods bought were entered twice in a supplier's account in the purchases ledger	
(b) Goods returned were not entered in the purchases ledger control account	
(c) Goods returned were entered twice in a supplier's account in the purchases ledger	
(d) Discounts received were not entered in a supplier's account in the purchases ledger	
(e) A bank payment to a supplier was entered into the wrong supplier's account in the purchases ledger	
(f) A bank payment to a supplier was entered twice in the purchases ledger control account	

(d) This is a summary of transactions with credit customers during December.

Transactions	Amount £
Balance due at 1 December	18,174
Goods sold	12,398
Bank payments received	11,053
Irrecoverable debts written off	295

Record these transactions in the sales ledger control account and show the balance carried down.

Select your entries for the details column from the following list: Balance b/d, Balance c/d, Bank, Discounts allowed, Discounts received, Irrecoverable debts, Purchases, Purchases returns, Sales, Sales returns.

Sales ledger control

Details	Amount £	Details	Amount £
Total		Total	

Task 6

The bank statement and cash book for July are shown below.

Check the bank statement against the cash book and enter:

* any transactions into the cash book as needed
* the cash book balance carried down at 31 July and brought down at 1 August

Bank Statement				
Date	**Details**	**Paid out**	**Paid in**	**Balance**
20-4		£	£	£
1 Jul	Balance b/f			1,180 D
2 Jul	Cheque 100150	556		1,736 D
3 Jul	Cheque 100151	862		2,598 D
4 Jul	Counter credit		3,170	572 C
8 Jul	Cheque 100153	168		404 C
10 Jul	Direct debit: NTL	110		294 C
12 Jul	Cheque 100152	785		491 D
13 Jul	Counter credit		2,563	2,072 C
18 Jul	Cheque 100154	129		1,943 C
20 Jul	BACS Credit: Citron plc		2,047	3,990 C
23 Jul	Direct debit: Transenergy	520		3,470 C
24 Jul	Cheque 100155	1,005		2,465 C
25 Jul	Counter credit		2,943	5,408 C
28 Jul	Bank charges	62		5,346 C
31 Jul	BACS: Wages	5,236		110 C
D = Debit C = Credit				

Cash book

Date 20-4	Details	Bank £	Date 20-4	Cheque number	Details	Bank £
4 Jul	Carpenter Ltd	3,170	1 Jul		Balance b/f	1,736
13 Jul	King plc	2,563	1 Jul	100151	Arma Trading	862
25 Jul	Murray Ltd	2,943	6 Jul	100153	K Bush	168
			7 Jul	100152	Hynde Music	785
			10 Jul	DD	NTL	110
			13 Jul	100154	Lennox & Co	129
			24 Jul	100155	A Adkins	1,005
			31 Jul	BACS	Wages	5,236

Select your entries for the details column from the following list: A Adkins, Arma Trading, Balance b/d, Balance c/d, Bank charges, K Bush, Carpenter Ltd, Closing balance, Hynde Music, King plc, Lennox & Co, Murray Ltd, NTL, Opening balance, Wages.

Task 7

Below is the bank statement for September.

BANK STATEMENT				
Date **20-4**		**Paid out** £	**Paid in** £	**Balance** £
01 Sep	Balance b/f			7,635 C
04 Sep	Cheque 100185	1,655		5,980 C
07 Sep	Counter credit		1,992	7,972 C
09 Sep	Cheque 100186	159		7,813 C
10 Sep	Direct debit: NTL	110		7,703 C
19 Sep	Cheque 100187	1,029		6,674 C
24 Sep	Direct debit: Transenergy	520		6,154 C
24 Sep	Cheque 100189	1,510		4,644 C
26 Sep	Counter credit		2,464	7,108 C
30 Sep	BACS: Wages	6,143		965 C
D = Debit C =Credit				

The cash book as at 30 September is shown below.

Date 20-4	Details	Bank £	Date 20-4	Cheque number	Details	Bank £
1 Sep	Balance b/f	7,635	1 Sep	100185	Tunstall plc	1,655
7 Sep	J Stone	1,992	6 Sep	100186	K Bush	159
26 Sep	Murray Ltd	2,464	10 Sep	DD	NTL	110
30 Sep	Davies Ltd	411	13 Sep	100187	Lennox & Co	1,029
30 Sep	Twain Trading	676	20 Sep	100188	Harris Ltd	600
			24 Sep	DD	Transenergy	520
			24 Sep	100189	MacColl Ltd	1,510
			28 Sep	100190	Simone & Co	342
			30 Sep	BACS	Wages	6,143

The cash book and bank reconciliation statement for September have not yet been finalised.

(a) Identify the **four** transactions that are included in the cash book but missing from the bank statement and complete the bank reconciliation statement below as at 30 September.

Do not enter minus signs or brackets in this task.

Select your entries from the following list:
K Bush, Davies Ltd, Harris Ltd, Lennox & Co, MacColl Ltd, Murray Ltd, Simone & Co, NTL, J Stone, Transenergy, Tunstall plc, Twain Trading, Wages.

Bank reconciliation statement	£
Balance as per bank statement	
Add	
Total to add	
Less	
Total to subtract	
Balance as per cash book	

(b) Refer to the cash book on the previous page and check that the bank statement has been correctly reconciled by calculating:

- the balance carried down

- the total of each of the bank columns after the balance carried down has been recorded

Balance carried down £	Bank column totals £

Task 8

A suspense account has been opened with a balance of £100.

The error has been identified as an entry made in the general ledger from the incorrectly totalled VAT column on the debit side of the cash book shown below.

Cash book – debit side

Date 20-4	Details	VAT £	Bank £
30 June	Balance b/f		6,883
30 June	Sumana & Co		545
30 June	Cash sales	88	440
30 June	Davies Ltd		640
30 June	Cash sales	104	520
	Totals	292	9,028

(a) Record the journal entries needed to:

- remove the incorrect entry
- record the correct entry
- remove the suspense account balance

Do not enter a zero in unused debit or credit column cells.

Select your account name from the following list: Cash book, Cash sales, Davies Ltd, Purchases, Purchases day book, Purchases ledger control, Purchases returns, Purchases returns day book, Purchases ledger control, Purchases returns, Purchases returns day book, Sales, Sales day book, Sales ledger control, Sales returns, Sales returns day book, Sumana & Co, Suspense, VAT.

Journal to remove the incorrect entry

Account name	Debit £	Credit £

Journal to record the correct entry

Account name	Debit £	Credit £

Journal to remove the suspense account balance

Account name	Debit £	Credit £

(b)   Another error has been found in the general ledger. Entries to record the purchase of office equipment for £950 paid from the bank have been reversed.

Record the journal entries needed to:

- remove the incorrect entry

- record the correct entry

Do not enter a zero in unused debit or credit column cells.

Select your account names from the following list: Bank, Cash, Office equipment, Purchases, Purchases ledger control, Sales, Sales ledger control, Suspense, VAT.

Journal to remove the incorrect entries

Account name	Debit £	Credit £

Journal to record the correct entries

Account name	Debit £	Credit £

Task 9

The journal entries below have been prepared to correct an error.

Journal

Account name	Debit £	Credit £
Purchases returns	562	
Suspense		562
Suspense	265	
Purchases returns		265

Record the journal entries in the general ledger accounts below and show the balance carried down in the purchases returns account.

Select your entries for the details column from the following list: Balance b/d, Balance c/d, Bank, Purchases returns, Suspense.

Purchases returns

Details	Amount £	Details	Amount £
		Balance b/f	2,048
		Purchases returns day book	854

Suspense

Details	Amount £	Details	Amount £
Balance b/f	297		

Task 10

On 30 November a trial balance was extracted and did not balance. The debit column totalled £177,443 and the credit column totalled £178,542.

(a) What entry is needed in the suspense account to balance the trial balance?

Do not enter a zero in the unused column cell.

Account name	Debit £	Credit £
Suspense		

(b) The journal entries to correct all the bookkeeping errors, and a list of balances as they appear in the trial balance, are shown below.

Journal

Account name	Debit £	Credit £
Office equipment	1,000	
Suspense		1,000
Sales	99	
Suspense		99
Bank charges	52	
Bank interest received		52
Bank charges	52	
Interest received		52

Complete the table below to show:
- the balance of each account after the journal entries have been recorded
- whether each balance will be a debit or credit entry in the trial balance

List of balances

Account name	Original balance £	New balance £	Debit in trial balance	Credit in trial balance
Office equipment	6,250			
Sales	89,361			
Bank charges	843			
Bank interest received	110			

(c) On 31 July a partially prepared trial balance had debit balances totalling £143,023 and credit balances totalling £125,375. The accounts below have not yet been entered into the trial balance.

Complete the table below to show whether each balance will be a debit or credit entry in the trial balance.

Account name	Balance £	Debit in trial balance	Credit in trial balance
Capital	25,672		
Bank loan	12,000		
Vehicles	20,024		

(d) What will be the totals of each column of the trial balance after the balances in (c) have been entered?

Account name	Debit £	Credit £
Totals		

Answers to practice assessment 1

Task 1

(a)

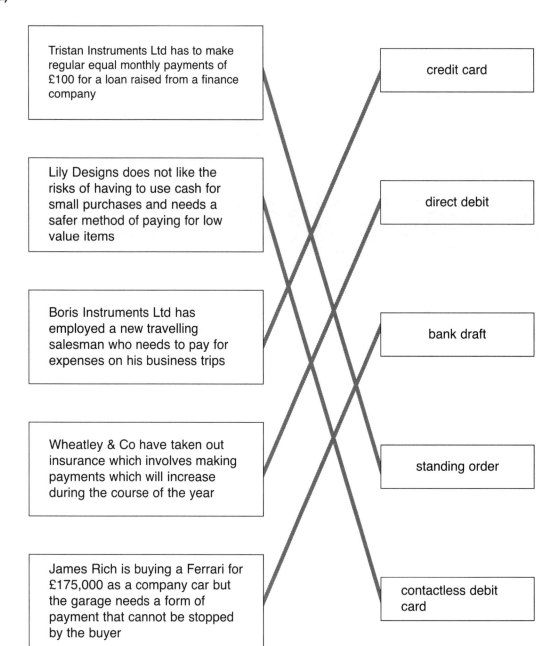

Tristan Instruments Ltd has to make regular equal monthly payments of £100 for a loan raised from a finance company

Lily Designs does not like the risks of having to use cash for small purchases and needs a safer method of paying for low value items

Boris Instruments Ltd has employed a new travelling salesman who needs to pay for expenses on his business trips

Wheatley & Co have taken out insurance which involves making payments which will increase during the course of the year

James Rich is buying a Ferrari for £175,000 as a company car but the garage needs a form of payment that cannot be stopped by the buyer

credit card

direct debit

bank draft

standing order

contactless debit card

(b)

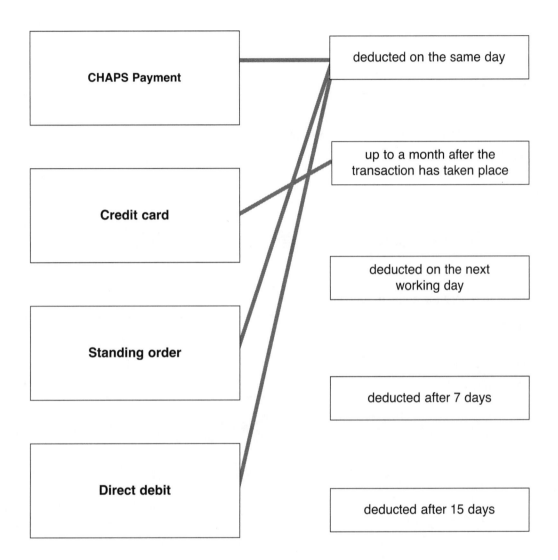

(c) (a) will not cause an imbalance; (b), (c) and (d) will cause an imbalance.

(d) (a) Error of original entry; (b) Error of omission; (c) Error of commission

(e) Correction of errors

Task 2

Journal to record the HM Revenue & Customs liability

Account name	Debit £	Credit £
Wages control	11,480	
HM Revenue & Customs		11,480

Journal to record the net wages paid to employees

Account name	Debit £	Credit £
Wages control	25,867	
Bank		25,867

Tutorial note: £40,827 – £4,780 – £3,840 – £2,860 – £1,740 – £1,740 = £25,867.

Journal to record the pension fund liability

Account name	Debit £	Credit £
Wages control	3,480	
Pension fund		3,480

Task 3

(a)

Journal

Account name	Debit £	Credit £
Irrecoverable debts	920	
VAT control	184	
Sales ledger control		1,104

(b)

Journal

Account name	Amount £	Debit £	Credit £
Fixtures and fittings	7,500	7,500	
Bank overdraft	2,150		2,150
Capital	10,000		10,000
Sales ledger control	4,650	4,650	

Task 4

(a)

Transaction	Amount £	Debit	Credit
VAT owing to HM Revenue & Customs at 1 July	1,585		✔
VAT total in the sales day book	2,627		✔
VAT total in the purchases day book	1,345	✔	
VAT total in the purchases returns day book	286		✔
VAT total in the discounts received day book	154		✔
VAT total in the cash book for cash sales	728		✔
VAT total in the petty cash book for expenses	22	✔	
VAT payment made to HM Revenue & Customs	1,585	✔	

(b)

Amount £	Debit	Credit
2,308		✔

Task 5

(a)   £16,231

(b)   £585

(c)   (a)   Goods bought were entered twice in a supplier's account in the purchases ledger

   (f)   A bank payment to a supplier was entered twice in the purchases ledger control account

(d)   **Sales ledger control**

Details	Amount £	Details	Amount £
Balance b/d	25,614	Bank	19,317
Sales	14,385	Sales returns	2,065
		Balance c/d	18,617
Total	39,999	Total	39,999

Task 6

CASH BOOK

Date 20-4	Details	Bank £	Date 20-4	Cheque number	Details	Bank £
1 Jun	Balance b/f	1,487	1 Jun	114117	Hendric & Co	395
4 Jun	Cottle Ltd	4,806	1 Jun	114118	Harrup & Noyes	1,310
20 Jun	W Waugh	2,108	10 Jun	114119	Farr Ltd	2,218
24 Jun	Pardo Ltd	1,746	18 Jun	114120	Bradnock Trading	1,036
24 Jun	Torre & Co	542	18 Jun	114121	Paxtons	1,427
21 Jun	Bayer Ltd	1,095	18 Jun	114122	Filiaps Ltd	798
21 Jun	Allen plc	2,786	20 Jun		Wyvern Council	235
			22 Jun		JA Finance	592
			28 Jun		Bank charges	45
			30 Jun		Balance c/d	6,514
		14,570				14,570
1 Jul	Balance b/d	6,514				

Task 7

(a)

Bank reconciliation statement	£
Balance as per bank statement	2,491
Add:	
W Waugh	946
Preston Ltd	247
Total to add	1,193
Less:	
O Borne	760
Filiaps	1,055
Total to subtract	1,815
Balance as per cash book	1,869

(b)

Balance carried down		Bank column totals	
	£		£
	1,869		5,436

Task 8

(a)   **Journal to remove the incorrect entry**

Account name	Debit	Credit
	£	£
Purchases ledger control	4,760	

Journal to record the correct entry

Account name	Debit	Credit
	£	£
Purchases ledger control		5,760

Journal to remove the suspense account balance

Account name	Debit	Credit
	£	£
Suspense	1,000	

(b)   **Journal to remove the incorrect entries**

Account name	Debit	Credit
	£	£
Bank	220	
Commission received		220

Journal to record the correct entries

Account name	Debit	Credit
	£	£
Bank	220	
Commission received		220

Task 9

Vehicles

Details	Amount £	Details	Amount £
Balance b/f	28,240	Suspense	10,650
Bank	12,385	Balance c/d	40,535
Suspense	10,560		
	51,185		51,185

Suspense

Details	Amount £	Details	Amount £
Vehicles	10,650	Balance b/f	90
		Vehicles	10,560
	10,650		10,650

Task 10

(a)

Account name	Debit £	Credit £
Suspense		950

(b) **List of balances**

Account name	Original balance £	New balance £	Debit in trial balance	Credit in trial balance
Rent paid	7,055	5,605	✔	
Purchases	65,032	65,532	✔	
Office expenses	9,536	9,786	✔	
Bank (overdraft)	2,088	2,338		✔

(c)

Account name	Balance £	Debit in trial balance	Credit in trial balance
Purchases returns	1,247		✔
Petty cash	68	✔	
Drawings	7,220	✔	

(d)

Account name	Debit £	Credit £
Totals	184,626	184,626

Answers to practice assessment 2

Task 1

(a)

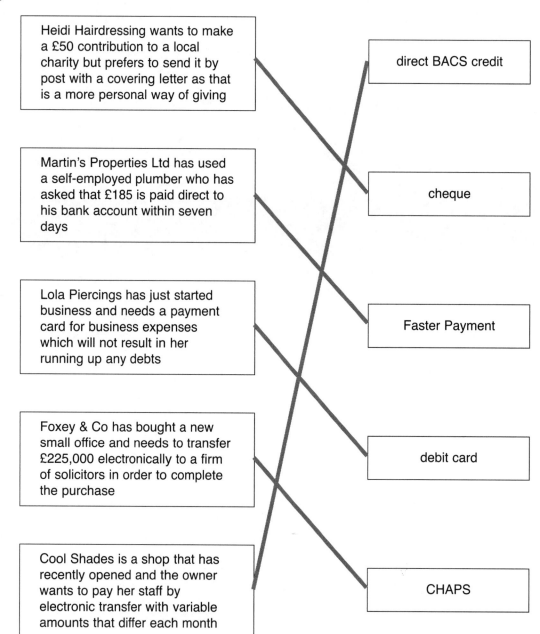

Heidi Hairdressing wants to make a £50 contribution to a local charity but prefers to send it by post with a covering letter as that is a more personal way of giving	direct BACS credit
Martin's Properties Ltd has used a self-employed plumber who has asked that £185 is paid direct to his bank account within seven days	cheque
Lola Piercings has just started business and needs a payment card for business expenses which will not result in her running up any debts	Faster Payment
Foxey & Co has bought a new small office and needs to transfer £225,000 electronically to a firm of solicitors in order to complete the purchase	debit card
Cool Shades is a shop that has recently opened and the owner wants to pay her staff by electronic transfer with variable amounts that differ each month	CHAPS

(b)

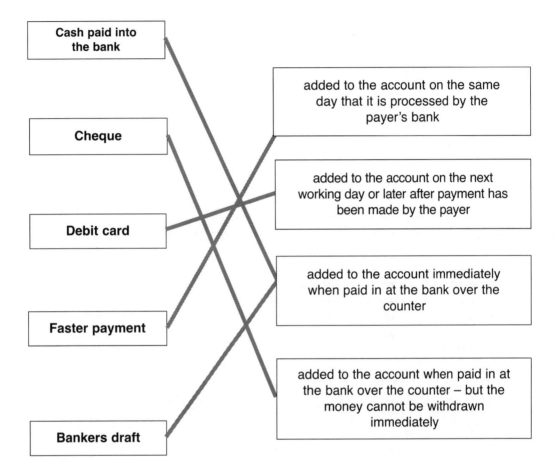

Cash paid into the bank	added to the account on the same day that it is processed by the payer's bank
Cheque	added to the account on the next working day or later after payment has been made by the payer
Debit card	added to the account immediately when paid in at the bank over the counter
Faster payment	added to the account when paid in at the bank over the counter – but the money cannot be withdrawn immediately
Bankers draft	

(c)   (a), (b), and (c) will cause an imbalance; (d) will not cause an imbalance.

(d)   (a) Error of principle; (b) Reversal of entries; (c) Error of original entry

(e)   Opening entries for a new business

Task 2

Journal to record HM Revenue & Customs liability

Account name	Debit £	Credit £
Wages control	5,158	
HM Revenue & Customs		5,158

Journal to record the net wages paid to employees

Account name	Debit £	Credit £
Wages control	12,608	
Bank		12,608

Tutorial note: £17,966 − £1,730 − £1,620 − £1,808 − £200 (£20 x 10 employees) = £12,608.

Journal to record the trade union liability

Account name	Debit £	Credit £
Wages control	200	
Trade union		200

Task 3

(a)

Journal

Account name	Debit £	Credit £
Irrecoverable debts	1,300	
VAT control	260	
Sales ledger control		1,560

(b)

Journal

Account name	Amount £	Debit £	Credit £
Office equipment	5,650	5,650	
Cash at bank	850	850	
Capital	4,000		4,000
Loan from bank	2,500		2,500

Task 4

(a)

Transaction	Amount £	Debit	Credit
VAT refund due from HM Revenue & Customs at 1 June	1,021	✔	
VAT total in the sales day book	1,854		✔
VAT total in the purchases day book	1,397	✔	
VAT total in the sales returns day book	159	✔	
VAT total in the discounts allowed day book	76	✔	
VAT total in the cash book for cash sales	528		✔
VAT total in the petty cash book for expenses	36	✔	
VAT receipt from HM Revenue & Customs	1,021		✔

(b)

Amount £	Debit	Credit
84	✔	

Task 5

(a) £11,926

(b) £872

(c) (a) Goods sold have not been entered in the customers' accounts in the sales ledger

(f) Irrecoverable debts written off have not been entered in the sales ledger control account

(d) Purchases ledger control

Details	Amount £	Details	Amount £
Bank	15,147	Balance b/d	18,976
Purchases returns	1,034	Purchases	10,325
Balance c/d	13,120		
Total	29,301	Total	29,301

Task 6

CASH BOOK

Date 20-4	Details	Bank £	Date 20-4	Cheque number	Details	Bank £
1 June	Balance b/f	15,189	1 June	111042	Prime kitchens	10,000
16 June	Britten & Bond	175	1 June	111043	Equipdirect	1,420
20 June	Macklin Ltd	950	1 June	111044	Long and Lane	80
21 June	Randle Fitments	300	1 June	111045	BLH Ltd	795
12 June	Cabot and Co	571	2 June	111046	MVR Ltd	652
			2 June	111047	Fairfield Ltd	2,500
			13 June	111048	Makin and King	450
			13 June		LMBC	150
			20 June		Insurance Direct	850
			23 June		Bank charges	88
			26 June		Overdraft fees	30
			30 June		Balance c/d	170
		17,185				17,185
1 July	Balance b/d	170				

Task 7

(a)

Bank reconciliation statement	£
Balance as per bank statement	752
Add:	
Barber Bates Ltd	469
Jackson & Co	245
Total to add	714
Less:	
Bridge Tools	607
Tenon Ltd	1,505
Total to subtract	2,112
Balance as per cash book	646

(b)

Balance carried down		Bank column totals	
	£		£
	646		5,411

Task 8

(a) Journal to remove the incorrect entry

Account name	Debit £	Credit £
VAT		1,100

Journal to record the correct entry

Account name	Debit £	Credit £
VAT	1,000	

Journal to remove the suspense account balance

Account name	Debit £	Credit £
Suspense	100	

(b) Journal to remove the incorrect entries

Account name	Debit £	Credit £
Heat and light	350	
Bank		350

Journal to record the correct entries

Account name	Debit £	Credit £
Heat and light	350	
Bank		350

Task 9

Rent paid

Details	Amount £	Details	Amount £
Balance b/f	12,360	Suspense	1,520
Bank	1,050	Balance c/d	13,140
Suspense	1,250		
	14,660		14,660

Suspense

Details	Amount £	Details	Amount £
Rent paid	1,520	Balance b/f	270
		Rent paid	1,250
	1,520		1,520

Task 10

(a)

Account name	Debit £	Credit £
Suspense		1,445

(b)   **List of balances**

Account name	Original balance £	New balance £	Debit in trial balance	Credit in trial balance
Office stationery	3,027	3,382	✔	
Rent received	8,040	9,840		✔
Telephone	1,285	1,735	✔	
Bank (overdraft)	3,261	3,711		✔

(c)

Account name	Balance £	Debit in trial balance	Credit in trial balance
Sales returns	1,364	✔	
Discounts received	728		✔
VAT (owing to HM Revenue & Customs)	2,390		✔

(d)

Account name	Debit £	Credit £
Totals	154,622	154,622

Answers to practice assessment 3

Task 1

(a)

The system set up by the banks for same day large payments is the **CHAPS** system.

If the amount to be paid electronically is smaller the bank **Faster Payment** system should be used.

For repeated electronic payments the banks offer a **standing order** which is suitable for situations when the amount and time interval is always the same.

The banks also offer the **direct debit** system when the amounts and time intervals can vary. The bank that sets up the payment in this case is the bank that **receives the payment**.

Direct credits are used for variable electronic payments, payroll payments for example. These are set up by the bank that **makes the payment**.

Plastic cards are also used to make payments. Transactions using a **debit card** are deducted from the bank account on the next day and a **credit card** allows monthly settlement to be made for the total expenses incurred during that month.

(b)

Payment method	Deduction from the bank account
cheque	**three working days later or more**
cash withdrawal from bank	**same day**
CHAPS	**same day**
credit card	**up to a month after the transaction date**
Faster Payment	**same day**

(c)   (a) and (b) will cause an imbalance; (c) and (d) will not.

(d)   (a) Error of principle; (b) Compensating error; (c) Error of commission

(e)   (d) A book of prime entry to record non-regular transactions

Task 2

Journal to record the net wages paid to employees

Account name	Debit £	Credit £
Wages control	36,864	
Bank		36,864

Journal to record HM Revenue & Customs liability

Account name	Debit £	Credit £
Wages control	9,959	
HM Revenue & Customs		9,959

Tutorial note: £50,176 – £4,798 – £2,467 – £2,694 – £2,321 – £1,032 = £36,864.

Journal to record the pension fund liability

Account name	Debit £	Credit £
Wages control	3,353	
Pension fund		3,353

Task 3

(a)

Journal

Account name	Debit £	Credit £
Irrecoverable debts	950	
VAT control	190	
Sales ledger control		1,140

(b)

Journal

Account name	Amount £	Debit £	Credit £
Capital	10,000		10,000
Bank loan	2,500		2,500
Computer equipment	8,620	8,620	
Inventory	3,880	3,880	

Task 4

(a)

Transaction	Amount £	Debit	Credit
VAT owing to HM Revenue & Customs at 1 November	2,735		✔
VAT total in the sales day book	3,192		✔
VAT total in the purchases day book	2,085	✔	
VAT total in the purchases returns day book	176		✔
VAT total in the discounts allowed day book	105	✔	
VAT total in the cash book for cash purchases	85	✔	
VAT on purchase of computers for use in the office	947	✔	
VAT payment made to HM Revenue & Customs	2,735	✔	

(b)

Amount £	Debit	Credit
1,787		✔

Task 5

(a)   £19,081

(b)   £186

(c)   (b)   Goods returned were not entered in the purchases ledger control account

       (c)   Goods returned were entered twice in a supplier's account in the purchases ledger

(d)   Sales ledger control

Details	Amount £	Details	Amount £
Balance b/d	18,174	Bank	11,053
Sales	12,398	Irrecoverable debts	295
		Balance c/d	19,224
Total	30,572	Total	30,572

Task 6

CASH BOOK

Date 20-4	Details	Bank £	Date 20-4	Cheque number	Details	Bank £
4 Jul	Carpenter Ltd	3,170	1 Jul		Balance b/f	1,736
13 Jul	King plc	2,563	1 Jul	100151	Arma Trading	862
25 Jul	Murray Ltd	2,943	6 Jul	100153	K Bush	168
20 Jul	Citron plc	2,047	7 Jul	100152	Hynde Music	785
			10 Jul	DD	NTL	110
			13 Jul	100154	Lennox & Co	129
			24 Jul	100155	A Adkins	1,005
			31 Jul	BACS	Wages	5,236
			23 Jul	DD	Transenergy	520
			28 Jul		Bank charges	62
			31 Jul		Balance c/d	110
		10,723				10,723
1 Aug	Balance b/d	110				

Task 7

(a)

Bank reconciliation statement	£
Balance as per bank statement	965
Add:	
Davies Ltd	411
Twain Trading	676
Total to add	1,087
Less:	
Harris Ltd	600
Simone & Co	342
Total to subtract	942
Balance as per cash book	1,110

(b)

Balance carried down	£	Bank column totals	£
	1,110		13,178

Task 8

(a)   Journal to remove the incorrect entry

Account name	Debit £	Credit £
VAT	292	

Journal to record the correct entry

Account name	Debit £	Credit £
VAT		192

Journal to remove the suspense account balance

Account name	Debit £	Credit £
Suspense		100

(b)   Journal to remove the incorrect entries

Account name	Debit £	Credit £
Office equipment	950	
Bank		950

Journal to record the correct entries

Account name	Debit £	Credit £
Office equipment	950	
Bank		950

Task 9

Purchases returns

Details	Amount £	Details	Amount £
Suspense	562	Balance b/f	2,048
Balance c/d	2,605	Purchases returns day book	854
		Suspense	265
	3,167		3,167

Suspense

Details	Amount £	Details	Amount £
Balance b/f	297	Purchases returns	562
Purchases returns	265		
	562		562

Task 10

(a)

Account name	Debit £	Credit £
Suspense	1,099	

(b) **List of balances**

Account name	Original balance £	New balance £	Debit in trial balance	Credit in trial balance
Office equipment	6,250	7,250	✔	
Sales	89,361	89,262		✔
Bank charges	843	947	✔	
Bank interest received	110	214		✔

(c)

Account name	Balance £	Debit in trial balance	Credit in trial balance
Capital	25,672		✔
Bank loan	12,000		✔
Vehicles	20,024	✔	

(d)

Account name	Debit £	Credit £
Totals	163,047	163,047

for your notes

for your notes

for your notes